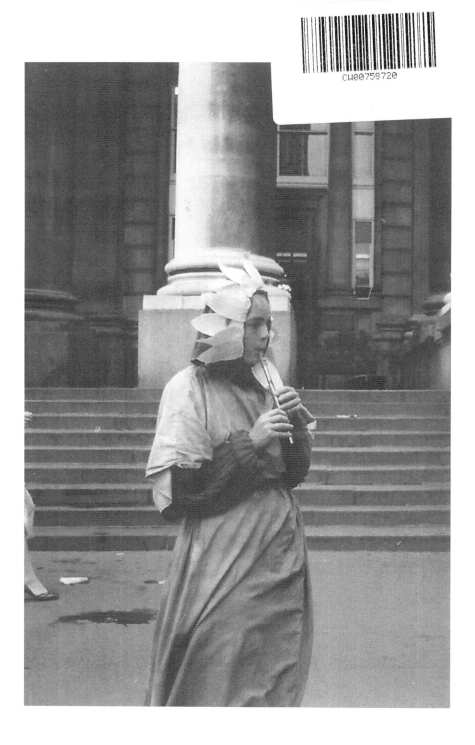

The Lonely Crowd
New Home of the Short Story

Edited and Designed by John Lavin

Advisory Editor, Michou Burckett St. Laurent

Cover image, 'The Man Who Had Always Wanted to Travel' by Constantinos Andronis (www.c-andronis.gr)

Frontispiece taken from 'Till Human Voices Wake Us' by Jo Mazelis

Published by The Lonely Press, 2015

Printed in Wales by Gwasg Gomer

ISBN 978-0-9932368-0-8

If you would like to subscribe to The Lonely Crowd please visit
www.thelonelycrowd.org / the-lonely-store
If you would like to advertise in The Lonely Crowd please email
ads@thelonelycrowd.org

Please direct all other enquiries to johnlavin@thelonelycrowd.org

Visit our website for more new short fiction, poetry and artwork
The Lonely Crowd.org

THE

LONELY

CROWD

Contents

Ballooning with Habibi
Stevie Davies

My eye snags on the close-up of a policeman's boot planted in the groin of a bearded protester. His face twists in anguish; my eyes water.

'What is it?' asks my mother. 'It's not Habibi, is it, Matt?'

'No. It's one of the Moslem Brothers.'

'Oh, bless him. Don't eat your heart out now. Habibi's like his cats. Nine lives.'

Habibi's blog has been down for a week. The loveliest and liveliest of men, gentle and funny and shrewd, he entered my heart five years back at the temple of Karnak. And that was it: although neither of us is prepared to abandon his native land, Habibi's my life. We've fallen into a rhythm, passionately together and tenderly apart. An open relationship, of sorts. There are questions we don't ask of one another.

Habibi was the nickname of the chubby guy on his knees in the Temple of Mut, the mother goddess, waving his arms as he discussed with American archaeologists the removal of earlier digs' debris from the West Porch. The detritus was littered with objects jettisoned by earlier excavators. Habibi's hand cradled the mould for a wedjat eye amulet, the right eye of Horus, with its falcon marking and a single teardrop.

I introduced myself. *'Salaam aleicum.* I'm Matt Oliver.'

'Aleicum salaam, Matthew. Aziz Halabi. But everyone calls me Habibi.' I gave him my hand as he scrambled up: the first time I touched Habibi. 'What a pleasure! - I am your greatest fan!' He held out the mould and launched into a spree of slightly wacky English. 'A lucky charm! Junked by some addled egg of a so-called archaeologist. Take it, Matthew, take it! Even the mould may have protective qualities. See the traces of blue on the clay?'

Before long we were one another's best friends. I'd known Habibi before I knew him. That, at least, was how I put it to myself. Doubtless most people feel the same. Whoever he touches goes away with a trace of turquoise on their clay. It's his vocation to collect the scattered world together.

Occasionally I've wondered: what underlies this genial warmth? I've seen Aziz's eyes grow cold and haunted. In some dark underground chamber, the membrane between innocence and cynicism becomes porous.

'Habibi! C'mon! Over here!' the Americans would yell when he waddled on to the temple site in the morning, cowboy hat atilt – 'Habibi!' - the equivalent of a chorus of 'Darling!'

Heads turned, not invariably with approval.

*

I phone but Aziz doesn't pick up. I'll just email again to check that the wadjet eye is doing its job.

Habibi is resistant to ideology; he fails to switch off his good humour when it would be politic to do so. Promiscuously tolerant, Habibi lacks something essential for survival in a world where the dictator has given place to the Brotherhood, and the Brotherhood to the Army, but where homophobia is constant, a kind of social glue. Aziz Halabi has piety, I know. He carries it lightly and privately beneath his multicoloured shirts. As the Revolution began, Habibi was on Tahrir Square. I trust he's keeping indoors nowadays and taking care of his cats.

The email is rejected; the blog's still down. I try Facebook. Nothing. He's been effaced.

That day at Karnak there was a dog lying in the temple. It seemed to have given up on hope. People kicked it as they went past.

Maybe the mongrel was dead. I didn't go and investigate. If it were alive, what could I have done for or with it? If dead, where would I bury it?

Fearing for Habibi, I also fear for the antiquities; for the survival of Egypt's mortuary world, our life's work. I read with dismay that Cairo Museum has been looted.

*

He was in my heart but I hadn't told him yet. Today was our museum day. Tomorrow would be our ballooning day. The following day I was booked to fly home.

Hardly were Habibi and I inside the museum than staff started chuckling. He hadn't said a thing as yet. Nothing absurd or jolly had passed his lips. It was as if a trace memory of Aziz Halabi's last visit had been awoken and the ripple effect went back and back into the building.

'It's Habibi!' the staff called to one another.

Cairo, under an acrid fog of fumes, was oppressively hot. We had no idea when we'd meet again.

'Do you believe in premonitions, Matt?' he asked.

I returned to him the mould for the eye amulet and closed his fingers round it. 'Put it in your pocket. To keep you safe, my darling.'

The 'darling' just came out. He showed no sign of noticing. Perhaps he took it as a straight translation of his nickname, though Habibi, a subtle linguist, knows there are no straight translations in this world. A lover of the Farsi poet Hafez, he's aware of how words slip and slide.

I'm unsure if my imminent departure had roused this sombre mood: possibly. Something remained unuttered, buried in a dark place. There's much in Habibi's life that he avoids discussing. Prejudices forbid him and his friends to live in the open. We weren't to know that soon the Revolution would break out on this very square, raising all manner of intemperate hopes.

First stop: the two thousand-year-old mummified cats. Their sacrificial effigies sat bolt upright in rows. Painted heads topped cylindrical bodies in containers, like children's ninepins. It was touching to see the whorls of the craftsmen's thumbprints in the bitumen-impregnated linen. Surely, I thought, these guys had moggies of their own at home and petted them as they sleeked round the family's legs. Staring feline faces were drawn on the masks, wearing a common expression, miffed and doleful, as well they might be. Terribly tiny, some of them: kittens, bred in factory-style catteries for slaughter and mummification.

'Sad little bods,' Habibi mused, on his haunches. 'It was a dog's life.'

I laughed. 'They adored cats though, didn't they? - like you. Killing them was a capital crime, unless one did it for a god.'

'Yes, these darling little chaps were for the chop. Only the best for Bastet.'

15

Bizarre to think of the millions raised for sacrifice and sale in the temple catteries, cadavers stacked in catacombs to appease the goddess. Bastet the super-cat was a war deity: you wouldn't want to cross her. One rake of those divine claws would blind or geld you. Life could turn – just like that - on ordinary folk: you had to keep your amulets and ankhs and spells in good working order.

Habibi's flat was overrun with rescue cats. I'd counted eleven, and other felines came and went, pressing themselves against the window, silhouetted against the sunset. Habibi transformed flea-infested, skeletal outsiders into creatures after his own rotund image. I'd barred them my bedroom, which they deeply resented.

'For goodness' sake pour me a glass of sacred Anathema,' he'd say as we lounged on cushions and the animals picked their way round and over us, thrumming with purrs, to drop senseless in a throbbing sea of fur. Alcohol, which his faith abhors, is relished by Habibi as God's gift. He feels it a positive duty to reproach the ignorant mullahs by enjoying a nice quaff, a jolly tipple, a rational sip, a festive glug, now and again. Wine loosens his tongue deliciously, in sprees of tasty English synonyms.

The thing I'd pledged myself to say had not been said. It wanted to be said. It begged me for release. It trembled, overdue, on my tongue-tip.

Outside the museum, chaos reigned. As archaeologists, we'd made our privileged way past the roaring sea of tourists – but now the dam was breached. Groups wrapped themselves around glass cases in the Tutankhamun hall, their guides competing to bellow information in diverse languages. The crowd fought itself.

Carried half off my feet, I lost sight of Habibi. When I located him, someone was crushed against his chest: I could only see the back of her head, with its shorn white hair, the pink scalp showing through. What was she confiding or imploring? Afterwards I thought: this lady had recognised in my friend a court of appeal; she'd glimpsed the turquoise smearing his common clay.

And then Habibi grinned. Ha! He reached inside his breast pocket.

When the alarm went off, an anxious tide of shushing travelled from wall to wall. 'Is it a bomb? Terrorists? Let's get the hell out.'

The invisible alarm hee-hawed, it brayed and raved from the region of Habibi's chest. Tourists funnelled out fast through the exit. The white-haired woman stepped back and chuckled and shook my friend's hand. Off she drifted towards Tut's bed, his game of senet and the other grave goods the boy king had taken along to wile away the tedium of eternity.

Guards arrived. Having switched off his alarm, Habibi greeted them as old pals. Whatever was up, he asked? The guilelessness portrayed by his cherub face looked decidedly fake. A senior official obviously thought so too.

'What was all that?' I asked him as we made for the exit.

'Tell you later.'

In Tahrir Square, traffic snarled in the usual way; motorbikes careered into gaps; vans mounted pavements; pedestrians wandered into the maelstrom and the relentless sun vomited heat. In what would come to be known round the world as Liberation Square, hopeful millions hadn't yet raised banners. Hosni Mubarak hadn't been toppled. The military had not fired upon demonstrators. Looters hadn't penetrated the museum. The National Party Headquarters were not yet burnt out.

'So?' I said.

Time, the lady from Toronto had told Habibi, shouting against the din. Time was running out: time she didn't have. Top of her bucket list since diagnosis was to view Tut's treasures. And here she was, with under a year to live – having journeyed so far – able, in this chaos, to see nothing, hear nothing.

'I used my nous, is all,' he said, shrugging.

I held Habibi's shoulders with both hands and softly drew him to me, kissing him gratefully on the mouth. In plain view. Darling, I said: my darling.

*

'It's OK,' I tell my mother. 'His blog's alive again, look.'

She bends to study the screen. 'Thank heaven he's safe. Habibi will ride it out, Matt, he's resourceful.'

Here's the photo, moon-face beaming - crinkling hair, darkly lustrous, long-lashed eyes, where comedy and compassion meet. I took the picture outside Cairo Museum, shortly after that first kiss. Five years back.

But why ever has he wiped the previous entries? Today's is captioned: 'Abominations! I anathematise!'

We both laugh aloud. Habibi always has this tonic effect.

There's a disease, the blogger announces, pervading every layer of society: it is the VICE of IRONY!

Which, if the reader is unfamiliar with the term, means: saying one thing while meaning the opposite. Double meaning! Lies! Bad faith! Irony is impure. Its tongue is forked. It is anathema.

'Bless him, he's on grand form!' says my mother. 'Denouncing puns and wordplay - *lascivious lubricious glossolalia!* Who in Britain knows words like that nowadays?' A pause. Then, 'Oh dear,' she says. 'Oh no.'

'What is it?'

He has previously erred, Aziz writes. He dreamed his way into Satan's dirty kennel of Irony. His tongue has resembled that of a dog – for all dogs are accurst - drooling strings of toxic saliva. That's why he has (penitent and ashamed) wiped the previous posts, which he formerly found so droll. That's why he renounces his impious nickname. That's why he's pledged to shun western double-talk.

Imagine the scene, he says, of enlightenment: you're in El-Marg, a Cairo suburb. You're a writer taking an evening stroll. But what's this? Police officers are raiding a health club, escorting out trouserless males. Whatever's going on, you wonder. Why are these criminals wearing only their immodest underpants? Imagine, the blogger writes, my disgust to discover that this so-called Health Club is a place of perversion! Fifteen criminals have been detained. Do such perverts deserve to live?

The blogger is relieved to learn of the referral of these criminals to the forensic medical authority for appropriate examination.

'Oh no,' says my mother. She turns away from the computer, hand over her mouth, and goes over to the window. 'They've taken over Habibi's blog,' she says. 'Haven't they?'

'Or he's writing under duress. To save his skin. The police are dictating.'

'How can one know?'

'One can't. '

'Where is he? What have they done to him?'

'I don't know.'

'How can we find out?'

'I don't know.'

No more quips and riffs from Habibi. Irony can go no further: it has reached the verge of the abyss. Is he still alive? Has he been tortured - subjected to degrading anal examinations – raped, in other words? Egypt's police, loathed under Mubarak, court popularity through witch-hunts directed at sexual scapegoats – and especially those with foreign links. Have I thoughtlessly opened him to danger? Habibi's power to be hurt sweeps over me; his gentleness.

There's an intimate pang, too, at glimpsing Habibi's way of life in my absence. A deep qualm. Draw the blinds, I think: it's best not to imagine. We agreed. We're free agents.

No, I'm not free; I never want to be free of Habibi.

Whatever has happened to the cats, I numbly wonder as I pack, with their keeper under arrest? They'd starve without their friend. If Aziz ever gets out – what's left of him - he'll stumble in through his front door upon the stench of cat corpses swarming with flies.

*

We ascended together at dawn, Habibi and I, over the Pyramids and the desert bathed in amber light. Aziz reached out, under the spell of the illusion, and touched my shoulder, then my hand, which he took warmly it in both of his. Then he

21

embraced and meltingly kissed me. I sneaked a glance round to make sure no one in the balloon was watching: it was my first, momentary, intimation that Habibi's world was closing in. But our fellow balloonists were in a trance of pleasure. Up there above the palm trees, looking down on the red and white keffiyehs of the camel-riders, we slowly rose together into a region of serenity, saying no word.

Everyone on the morning earth seemed, as we came floating down, to love one another. Endearments drifted up. Darling, they said, darling. Women baking bread, cross-legged on the ground, looked up and waved. Armed police strolled below us, arm in arm or coupled in a loose embrace.

Three Poems
Medbh McGuckian

THE SHAPE OF THIS HOW

The May litany is chanted
In the misty twilight edges of the fields.
They are lighting candles at cemeteries,
Priests are whispering.

The village name means 'frostbite'
Also, 'cuckoo bird'. There was a soldier's city
Somewhere on the outskirts of town
Past Apple, Pear and Plum Streets

Where everything was washed away
And the earth was so intelligent
As not to resist the birth
Of the new personality.

We rubbed our cloth shoes with chalk
Until they were shining white.
He would observe the weather through

The window, complained only to his diary.

Amid all the useless chatter,
To name one's child 'Belfast,'
I sprinkled some unborn poems
Over my forest brother's pestered head,

Mussing his hair, kneading his knees,
Sprayed with holy water.
Such a molten state of mind -
I grew up under his wing.

And now you will see
The frightened shadow of a cloud
Scurrying across the sublime
Pastoralism of his late poetry.

The poems approach us like a tawny
Iceberg. Take the sheepskin
Off your soul, watch
The coming and going of ships,

Dream peacefully
Under chestnut trees,
Rest in the silvery sand
Of the riverbank.

TREE PORTRAIT TAKEN AT DUSK

Blessed is he who left the banquet
Of life without drinking all the wine
In the glass - who didn't read his novel
To the end and was able to bid it farewell

At once. Pencils still lie
On the illuminated table in his room,
As if it were just another working day.
He rested quietly, a corpse

In sultry weather, but he was new
To death and looked as if he might
Get up and go about his business:
There was a small black hole in his temple.

His hands with their fingers upcurled
Seemed to have no connection to the rest
Of him. To see with the mind, this deep
Opening, to think with the eye his neglected

Grave, out of the as-found, that houses
Something that has not yet arrived.
To speak of the ghost and indeed to

And with it, beneath the undamaged

Chestnut trees, in the cemetery,
'In Paradisum', the built-in dappled
Shadows, the sage and peach silks
Of the garden, winter cherry and the dead

Leaf colour. We actually realise
How low the level of the ground is,
That is how it has been up to now,
Everything is there waiting for us.

Dark marks on the white bark.
The perfect silver edge of that
Magnetic balcony looking out
Over nothing, shot through with unprecedented

Dazzling figures. Neither the wind
In the opened up city, nor the leaf interest
Can make the city meaningful.
Nor the fact that the path keeps

Going till a tongue of the inside
Floor tastes clean sharp sand
Or first snow. The resurrection
Is not a door that exactly opens easily,

Unless for Saint Rita, patron of
The impossible. Death is possible
For everyone, more than being born
Or hearsay of it. How trees lift

Water to great heights.
There will be an empty
Setting at the already
Laid table: it is his.

THE ROCKET DOGS

Of the twelve dogs used, five perished.
They flew in pairs, all of them at least twice.
Their coats were light in colour to facilitate
Filming. They were confined to increasingly
Smaller cages, had their arteries rerouted,
Rats, mice, fruit flies, plants and rabbits
Were their crewmates.

Lemon, Linden, or Gnat, they had that
Inescapable cute factor, they whimpered
As the crane lifted their capsule on to
The ballistic missile. Inert and helpless
During the first moments of weightlessness,
They twitched convulsively and vomited
In their decaying orbit.

Their distinctive bleeps recovered them
Cold but alive, the Soviet children said
A camel should have been sent instead,
Some volunteered themselves.
The more time passes, the more
Sorry I am.

Old Ghost

Anna Metcalfe

Sitting under the most pathetic of all the pathetic-looking foothill trees, by the mountains that marked the edge of the village, Old Ghost was teaching me how to play 'Crazy Eights'.

'You have too much imagination; not enough strategy,' he said. 'And you're going to lose.'

&

'We're out of wine,' says Rina without looking in the fridge, so I know she has been drinking alone. Before I make any comment about it, she says: 'I'll go.' She throws on her coat and she goes.

&

Rina and I have three things in common: we are immigrants, we share a flat and we work irregular hours. Rina is an auxiliary nurse. I am a driver for the Hotel L'Amitié, a plush hotel in the heart of the 5th arrondissement. We do not live in the city itself but in Ivry sur Seine, which has a good end and a bad end and two metro stops. Our basement flat is smack in the centre of it all and is neither good nor bad. It is very small. There are two small bedrooms, a shower closet, and a bit in the middle with a sofa, an old television and a coffee table; then a corner that we call the kitchen, complete with microwave, fridge and sink. We keep our food in a small cabinet under the television or on the floor by the sink.

❧

Rina hates her job, handing out cups of water, taking urine samples and, in her words, cleaning up after everybody else. I like my job and I am respected for being reliable and available to work at all hours. Unlike the majority of my colleagues, I am not married and I do not have children. This is enough, for the moment, to make me a good employee. Mostly, I do 'transfers', shuttling back and forth to the airports, delivering tourists to the gaudy hotel foyer, with its shiny, green plants in ornamental plant pots, or taking them back to the concrete bays of the airport taxi rank, wondering at the ugliness of air travel, the clunkiness of all things international. Other tasks include chauffeuring guests to and from the major sites of interest: art galleries, monuments, places of worship, restaurants, cafés, boutiques, *les grands magasins*.

≈

I like the monotony of my work, the familiar roadways, the predictability of my clients. There are those who are silent, those who ask questions, and those who wish to be asked the particular questions that a female taxi driver is allowed to ask: Is this your first time in the city? Are you here on business? Will you be staying long? I have cultivated an unshakeable patience in the face of traffic jams, diversions and roadworks. I talk just enough to be charming for the sake of a decent tip but not so much that they remember who I am when they get out of the car. It is a strange kind of art.

≈

Rina comes back with the wine and pours us both a glass. She asks about my day and I tell her about a client I had to take to the Botanical Gardens. When we got there, he asked me to wait for him until he was ready to return to the Hotel de L'Amitié. I didn't have to wait very long. After ten minutes he reappeared, moving towards the car, almost at a run. His face was red and blotchy. As he got closer, I thought I saw a tear on one cheek but it might have been a drop of sweat gleaming in the afternoon sun as, although it was cold, he appeared quite flustered. Before he got in the back, he stopped to slap himself on the face a couple of times. He was tall, fairly handsome and well dressed: an appearance that seemed suddenly incongruous given his emotional disarray. When he finally opened the door of the car, he could not wait to confess his embarrassment. He explained, in English, how there was, in the garden, a series of large, banked flower beds with rows and rows of small yellow blooms growing close to the ground. They were the very same flowers that his mother had grown in the garden of his childhood home. As a boy, she had requested that, in the summer months, he urinate on the flowers to make them grow a little taller. A neighbour had told her the trick. He did as he was asked and, over time, the flowers did indeed increase in size and health. When he saw the very same flowers in the Botanical Gardens he felt an extraordinary urge to urinate over the whole damn lot, in honour of his mother. Torn between this desire -- which, he wished to emphasize, was extreme -- and the knowledge that this would be entirely inappropriate behaviour that could result in his being arrested or, at the very least, forced to leave, he fled the scene. It was the struggle between these two demands on his being at the gardens that was the cause of his distress.

On the way back to the hotel he pulled a set of clippers out of the inside pocket of his jacket and began to trim his finger nails. When we arrived at the hotel car park, he picked the small pieces of trimmed nail off his trousers and the seat of the car. He then placed them in a small, black pouch, which he returned to his inside pocket, along with the clippers. Later, when I inspected the car, it was almost spotless: just one tiny clipping of nail that I swept away with a tissue.

Rina says she does not know how I put up with all these imbeciles who have so much more money than sense. I say it makes things more interesting. Rina laughs.

'How was your day?' I say, but she ignores my question and talks again about her ex-husbands.

The first one is dead. Her biggest regret is that their marriage was almost over before he passed. She often says how, if only he'd died a month or two earlier, when things were all right, there'd be something to cling to. The second ex-husband, who is, in fact, technically her present husband, works with Rina at the hospital. He is a doctor. He is the reason she is here. They arrived together as economic migrants eighteen months into their marriage, just as the cracks in their relationship were beginning to show. They thought that if they could solve their money problems they could solve themselves. They were wrong. He left Rina for a twenty year old cook working in the hospital cafeteria, which means that Rina has to take a packed lunch with her every day. Now, he has no money problems at all while Rina has far more than she ever had at home. But she won't go back. Too stubborn.

I never tire of telling her she will meet someone new but Rina doesn't believe in the possibility of new chapters. After she has revealed her latest thoughts, she says it doesn't matter, it will all end up the same. Then she raises her hand and points a finger at me.

'Tell me about Old Ghost,' she says.

So I tell her the story of Old Ghost, which she has heard many times.

⁊

Tomorrow, I have to take a client to a place I have never driven to before, a fair way out of the city on the other side of Chateau de Vincennes. After I have told Rina the story about Old Ghost, I take down the atlas to check the route. It's pretty straightforward. As I slide my eyes across the map I see there is a bend in the river that reminds me of the river back home, the lazy curve it draws through the city.

'Rina,' I say, 'is there anything here that makes you feel like you're somewhere else?'

'What do you mean?' she says.

'Like a building, a window, a view. Something that reminds you of a different place and trips you up.'

'The embassy,' she says.

'Which one?' I ask.

'Russian,' she says. 'The big, Soviet front. Looks like my old town hall. We had assemblies there sometimes, for school, on special occasions.'

I feel glad that she has a connection to home and that the answer to my question came so readily. Certain places have a way of making other places more imaginable. Other places give the impression that their place is the only place on earth. Paris can do both, depending on the arrondissement, and the direction in which you are facing.

*

I don't trust maps anymore, though they have been the key to my survival in the city. If I picture a map of my homeland, I see the lines of its borders trembling, like the unfinished drawing of a child. Its mountainous regions and vast waterways are depicted in colours from smoke-grey to ink-black and the whole surface of it pulses like an open wound. People trickle out of the borders leaving trails of inky blackness behind them, marking out pathways over adjoining territories. Spots of ink reach all corners of the globe: microscopic, black dots, like bugs behind the glass of a picture frame.

Among all the black dots, there is one dot in particular that troubles me. That is, the one that marks the imagined movements of Old Ghost. The more I try to fix it, the more it shakes and wobbles until the whole thing becomes a terrible blur.

&

Old Ghost has taken on a particular significance for Rina, not as a person, but as an idea. It is not that he is alive or that he loves me that matters to her. It is the fact that she believes me when I say he is, or he was, kind and that his genre of kindness ever existed at all.

Old Ghost, I say to Rina, is the best man I have ever known. This is true, but I have not known very many men, at least, not very well. There is my brother, with whom I travelled and who also lives here, working in a bakery in the north part of the city. There is my father, now living on the other side of the world, with my mother, where they are safe. We no longer speak as for a long time he feared that any communication could put us all in danger. Now, our silence has become habit. If I were to write to him, I would not know what to say. He is a spiritual man and believes that — with or without regular conversation or letter writing — somehow we are still in touch. My brother hates him for abandoning us, for assuming that we could make it on our own. He finds his spiritual optimism patronising and unrealistic, while I sit somewhere in the middle, wanting to believe in everything my father says, while understanding the impracticability and impending danger of his ideals.

These are the men I have known. And Old Ghost. Although I have not heard from him since the blackout, my guess is that he is still very kind.

'Tell me how you met,' Rina says.

'At the school gates,' I say. 'He was my brother's friend.'

❧

Actually, he was not my brother's friend; he was trying to become my brother's friend, but my brother was smart, popular and good at sport, which meant that he was also influential and could afford to be picky. Old Ghost, quiet and overly polite, did not fit in. For several weeks, Old Ghost persisted, waiting for my brother to leave school to see if he could go with him to the cinema or the ice-cream shop or the basketball courts but my brother, despite understanding his silent pleas, walked past everyday without giving Old Ghost so much as a look.

I knew that it was best for me to walk behind, so that my brother could do as our parents bid him and drop me off at home, while at the same time pretending to have nothing to do with me. Old Ghost lived near us and, for a time, as I walked behind my brother, he walked a few paces behind me, placing himself beneath even me in the social rankings. Then one day he said hello and after that we walked together. This displeased my brother and made him suspicious but it did not displease him sufficiently to talk to our parents — who were, after all, engaged in far more important affairs — or to take his mind off his own concerns regarding the maintenance of his high status at school, the same status that would, eventually, give him the contacts he needed in order for us to make our escape.

Whatever I can say about my brother, he was the one to make sure I could get out while my father took care of my mother and himself, as ever, thinking it for the best to let us make it on our own.

'But when did you really make friends?' Rina wants the long version this time, with details and supporting evidence.

'There was a shop across the road from the school,' I say. 'I went in to buy a box of tea. Old Ghost followed me. He bought me a pack of cards. His father played a lot of cards and so he taught me his favourite games.'

'And you became friends,' Rina says.

'And we became friends. He was a like a teacher to me.'

'A teacher or a friend?'

'He helped me with my homework. He made me creative. He was as patient a person as you can imagine. He listened to me. He helped me to picture my dreams and make them real and solid things that I could have and hold and do and achieve and be.'

'When did he give you the maps?' says Rina.

'You're skipping ahead,' I say.

Rina shrugs. She fills her empty glass and tops mine to the brim. Rina drinks fast.

'I was fifteen. We were starting to talk about how and when to leave.'

'When you say we.'

'My brother and I.'

'Not Old Ghost,' Rina says.

'No,' I say.

'Did you always know you would leave him?'

'No,' I say. I don't like this. She knows.

'So tell me about the maps.'

I tell her about the maps.

&

You couldn't get maps of foreign places -- at least, not big ones with all the detail -- unless they were specially ordered to the library. While my brother talked only about the practicalities of leaving - and never the reality of arriving somewhere else - I wanted some security. I knew there were many things for which I would not be able to prepare myself, but there were also things I could learn that would make life easier upon arrival. I chose the roads. I could learn to find my way around the city, I decided, if only I had a map. So Old Ghost wrote a history project on this very place in order to get for me the maps that I required. I drew plan after plan of the roadways, some of which he used as illustrations in his work.

'And Old Ghost memorised the maps as well,' Rina says.

'No,' I say.

'So you always knew that he would not be coming?'

'No,' I say.

'But he didn't learn the roads? It doesn't make sense.'

'None of it makes sense. The whole thing is ridiculous. Would it ever occur to you to memorise a city you'd never seen?'

'No,' she says. 'How did you do it?'

I studied and I studied and I studied. It was a time in my life when I believed there was nothing I couldn't achieve by learning. Old Ghost held the maps up to his face and tested me. He would say things like: 'Take me from Canal Saint Thérèse' down to 'Le Musée de L'Art Brut' and I would get annoyed because he was giving me too many clues.

'What clues?' he would say.

And I would tell him: 'you said "down",' and he would apologise.

I would describe to him the roads and the roundabouts, the one-way systems and the lanes it was necessary to traverse in order to get from the one place to the other. Mostly, I was right. I had worked hard, after all. But if I made an error, he would always correct me, and always with kindness. He once said: 'Taxi drivers are usually men, you know,' but not in a way that made me think I couldn't do it. When he was old enough to use his father's car, he took me out to the disused corn fields and taught me how to drive an automatic. He said I was a quick learner, that there was nothing I couldn't do.

ﹶﹴ

'Why did he not leave when you left?' says Rina. I know what she is doing: she is pushing me to feel something so that she can feel something too.

'I was in danger and he was not,' I say. 'My parents were in trouble with the government, his were not.'

'But your parents thought you would be safe.'

'They thought that once they were gone we would be left alone. I would have believed them but my brother knew better.'

'And now?' Rina says. 'Will Old Ghost be safe now?'

I say nothing.

'Will he come, do you think? He knows where you are, after all.'

The question frightens me. Rina senses my fear and is herself afraid.

'He'll come,' she says, with a smile. 'I know it.'

'It's not that kind of story,' I say. 'He was like a brother.'

'You have a brother,' Rina says.

'A teacher, then.'

'You're too old for teachers, now.'

But these are the only kinds of men I can imagine.

&

I have changed my mind. I no longer wish to tell stories about the past. I want to talk only of the present; about my passengers and how, for a short time, I control the direction of their lives. They sit in the back of my car on the phone to this person, that, or the other. They say things like: 'I'm here safely, I'll call again soon, I'll see you next week.' They complain about how expensive it is now to call abroad. It should all be the same price. What's a bit of land, a stretch of water?

&

'Show me a photograph,' says Rina, though she knows that I have none.

I remember precisely when the photographs went missing. It was the first border crossing. The guards got us to unpack everything and then watched us as we packed it all up again. I had a small rucksack, and, pulling it onto my back, out of the corner of my eye, I saw something fall. I think I knew the photographs were gone. I could have bent down to look, to check it was not the photographs that were lying there on the ground, that it was just a tissue or an old receipt, but I did not.

Rather, I climbed back into the truck with my brother, linking my arm through his, pressing my body into it. He does not like me to touch him but over the month-long journey he never once complained. In any case, we left and when I look back now I wonder why I let the photographs go. I know that I must have done it on purpose, but I cannot fathom the reason.

*

Things were changing then in a way that I have only just begun to be able to describe. When travelling, it is difficult to note a shift in anything other than safety and terrain. With greater stability, however, it is possible to look back and mark the subtle changes taking place, remembering who I was before I left and taking stock of what I have become. I see now what I lost on the journey: some bright, essential thing, that gave me a kind of confidence I have not yet recovered.

I have decided that there are two different kinds of wanting to live. One is illogical, irrational and rude. It kicks in when there is nothing else left. The other is beautiful: a desire to be, a desire for others to be. It is this latter kind of wanting that I am slowly piecing together again and I do not know what the outcome will be; that is, I do not know if it will be the same as before.

*

The most notable side effect of my emotional restitution is dreaming. Every night, without fail, bright, fiery dreams.

I dream there is a split in the earth that cannot be crossed. There are no bridges and it is too deep and dangerous to climb down and then up because the earth at the bottom is too hot. I dream of a volcano throwing ash into the air so that all the planes hover round the city unable to land. I wait in my car looking up at the sky and wondering when my passengers will appear.

I dream we are standing at the school gate. Old Ghost is twelve or fifteen or twenty or sixty or more. I look at him as a guardian. I will do what he says. The school is empty. The security guards have gone home or are not yet there. The windows of the school are black and opaque. Old Ghost stands in front of the gate, blocking my way. He understands that we have stumbled upon the school while it is asleep, before it was meant to be found. The light is bright and getting brighter but still the desertion makes it feel as though it is night. Old Ghost leads me away from the dreadful school and into my next dream.

I dream we have a baby. It comes out grey and cries and cries until Old Ghost takes it away so that I cannot hurt it anymore.

I dream Old Ghost arrives and gets a job like Rina's, cleaning up vomit and blood and urine and the traces of dead people in the hospital beds.

I dream I am writing letters. I have the feeling I am made of air. The paper too, I sense, is air, as is the pen in my hand. The dream is bright and the edges of the paper are frightening, even though they are nothing but air. I am exhilarated by the possibilities of my dreams, the way materials do not behave as I expect. This makes me fearful but, at the same time, there is always the sense that, in dreaming, I already have everything I need. It is only upon waking that I feel a lack.

I dream Old Ghost is standing in front of a large glass window. There is a terrible wind outside and I am frightened that the glass will break under the pressure. I am standing in the doorway of the room behind, calling to Old Ghost to make him move away. There are cats, four or five of them, in the room behind me, brushing against my legs, making frightened noises of their own. The wind roars and the glass breaks in slow motion sending shards flying towards him. I shut the door of my room and cower behind it in the darkness with the cats climbing over my knees.

❧

Rina drains the last of the wine into her glass and goes to the cupboard to retrieve the second bottle.

'Do you still have the cards?' she says.

'The playing cards?' I say. This is a question she has not asked before.

'Yes,' she says.

I go to my room and pull the battered box of cards from the drawer in my bedside table.

'When did you last play?' Rina says.

'The journey here. We played a lot. There wasn't much else to do.'

'Which games?'

'All kinds.'

'The ones Old Ghost taught you?' says Rina.

'Sometimes,' I say.

'Can you teach me one?' says Rina.

'Yes,' I say, shuffling the cards in my hands.

Rina giggles like a child and moves her chair closer to mine as I place eight well-worn cards face down on the table.

For Those Who Come After
Gary Raymond

Prologue

Claus Julius was my lifeline. He didn't sound like the great emancipator down the phone, and he looked far from it in person, tall and grave on the doorstep; but he was all I had. I could feel the paycheque slipping away as each day passed until I took his call. I had been hired to write a biography of Ki Monroe – poet, visionary, satirist, enigma. *Enigma*, by God: there were chasmal holes in his story! Dead ends and misted decades the like of which I had not previously encountered. He was a man of whom the myth heavily outweighed the facts. I had always assumed that's why his estate had hired a journalist to write the book rather than an academic, a poetry professor from deep in the dusty halls. There was legwork to be done. They weren't to know the legwork would count for little as well.

I was at the edge of reason. Monroe did *this*, Monroe did *that*; there was a minor scandal or two, forgotten poetry, times past. He was a Bloomsbury outcast; was in Spain during the war; retired to a fishing village in Portugal when barely into middle age to farm and cast his net; died in a car accident in nineteen fifty. The advance was handsome, the story was not.

Claus Julius caught me in my office on a typically moribund day. I was tired, snappy, preparing to face the reality of my predicament more as every day went by. Our first conversation went something like this:

"You're an American?"

"Canadian," I said. "What can I do for you, Mr Julius?"

"I understand," he said. "I am Austrian. People assume I am a German always."

"I was just on my way out," I said.

"Mr Buren used to say that sooner or later you realise everybody is from somewhere else."

"Is that right?" I said.

"He used to say everybody is looking for adoption. What brings *you* to London?"

"It was *you* who called *me*, Mr Julius; and I don't have much time."

I could hear him sucking his teeth.

"You are writing a biography of Ki Monroe, are you not?"

"I am," I said. "And how can I be of help?"

"Are you finding it a difficult task? Frustrating?"

"It's all part of the process, Mr Julius."

This was my fifth biography: two movies stars, an aeronautical pioneer, a race car driver and now a poet.

"As I thought. Then you may be interested to see something that I have. My former employer, Mr Harold Buren, wrote a memoir. He knew Mr Monroe well."

"That name is not familiar to me," I said.

I looked across my study at the wall I had papered with little sticky notes; names, dates, events, in tasselled patterns of disjointed yellow shadow – a sight that had come to look more and more like a final curtain.

"It is not a name familiar to many. My former employer was a very private man."

"This Mr Buren is no longer with us, I take it? No longer able to speak with me personally?"

"Sadly Mr Buren passed away some years ago."

"And I don't know anything about this memoir, Mr Julius. I have read everything ever written on Monroe, twice over."

"Oh, dear; you misunderstand. It has not been published. I have the only manuscript under lock and key."

I opened the browser on my laptop.

"So how did your employer and Monroe know each other?" I said.

"They first met, so I understand, in the mid-nineteen thirties."

I typed Harold Buren's name into the search engine.

"So he was part of the Soho crowd?"

"He knew them," said Julius.

What came up on the browser was a surprising and suspicious lack of information. But there was a photograph. Harold Buren. A serious face, handsome, clean, long; his eyes were conspicuously blank, unsympathetic, but bold; it seemed to be a close-up from a group photo. Buren was a South African, like Monroe. His father died young and his mother brought the family to London. It seemed as if the cause of his wealth was, essentially, war; some speculative investment or other by his father in American armament firms and they hit the jackpot in nineteen fourteen. Harold Buren inherited these investments, had an astute mind for business and slowly added to his portfolio with gold and more arms. He never married. Never had children. Died in nineteen eighty four and left his money to an educational Trust in Spain. There was nothing else.

"It seems your Mr Buren would be an even more difficult subject to write about than my Mr Monroe," I said.

"Not if you read the manuscript I have," said Julius.

I thought for a moment. There is a point in these things when going deeper is the only way on offer.

"Why was this memoir never published?" I said.

"Mr Buren did not write it for publication. He wrote it as testament."

"Testament to whom?"

"Mr Buren was the last person to see Mr Monroe alive."

That had my attention: Monroe's death. His car went over a cliff. He was drunk at the wheel, coming back from a fishing trip.

"What do you mean he was the last person to see Monroe alive?" I said.

There was a pause; Julius sucked his teeth once more.

"It is not for me to say," said Julius. "You need to read the manuscript."

It got me to the house. Claypole: an enormous white Georgian building in central London. Julius was a tall man, old but fit, straight, but – and so confident was he around the halls of the house it was not immediately obvious – he was almost completely blind. I knew that his myopia was not absolute as he knew where to put his hand when I held out mine, but he held his head high, tilted back, and his pupils were a wintry grey. He explained his blindness as being only a slight concern at birth, and that it crept over him, through him, as the decades went on. His final blindness, he said, would be at the moment of death. He had been closing down since the day he was born, he said.

He was aging, now perhaps in his mid-seventies. Harold Buren had left him a small fortune (a pinprick into Buren's actual worth), as well as the house in which we stood, and as he felt it difficult to work for anyone else in the same capacity after Buren had died, he retired on his money and indulged in his hobby of restoring old books. I asked how a man with his particular impairment could carry out such delicate work. He said that he had steady hands and all the time in the world.

His study, on the ground floor, was lined with glowing old spines of forgotten tomes on every subject, from seventeenth century botany, to census documents, novels, journals, science manuals and ornithological sketch books, even Kama Sutras.

Julius had a steadiness to him that suggested he was more than able at his tasks – more able than a seeing man. Every movement was considered, a method that almost amounted to a sixth sense. Within the walls of the house that entombed him was a world of its own rules. There was a professional spirit, I figured, hanging over from his days as a valet, always having to be at hand, a man machine attuned to the atmosphere of the room. He had modified the design for this peacefulness into an artful attention to detail, to restoration – he could never fully appreciate the work he did on these books, and yet he didn't seem to have anyone else in mind.

He presented me with the Buren manuscript as if it was a sacred text and, at first inspection, inside was an example of delicate penmanship. The script was hand-written, hundreds and hundreds of pages without so much as a single alteration or blemish.

"This is the final draft?" I said.

"It is the *only* draft," said Julius. "Mr Buren was painstaking in its composition. It had to be a pure truth, you see."

"Could I take it?" I said.

"No," said Julius, softly. "But I will permit you to read it and make hand written notes. Here."

I'll admit, as I looked down at it, cast my eyes across several passages, it did not strike me as a breezy read.

"It may take some time," I said.

"There are plenty of rooms. You are welcome to be my guest."

A cavernous fatigue prevented me from negotiating the script out of Julius' possession, and I'm not sure I would have got anywhere even on top form.

I was still looking at Julius with a sideways glance. The whole encounter seemed from another era – he was dressed in a pin-striped three-piece suit with a fob chain, and yet, by his own admission, he spent most of his days alone in his big old house leaning over dilapidated manuscripts, carefully bringing them back from the dead, feeling his way through their scars.

He motioned for me to follow him and led me to a room up several flights of stairs and, placing his hand on the doorknob looked over his shoulder in my direction, his grey eyes like those of a snake, and he said, "This was Mr Buren's study for much of his later years."

We entered. Julius moved easily about the room lighting it by switching on the various and many lamps. The room was large, the walls of a deep, regal burgundy; towering columnal curtains hid tall narrow windows – it was like a gallery of a long lost era, an era of empires and ball gowns, but in place of young sharply dressed soldiers and beautiful debutantes were mismatched sofas and armchairs, all piled with loose papers and books and magazines. And in the centre of the room was a desk.

"There is no disputing Mr Buren's wealth," said Julius; "though some may have questioned his sanity toward the end. But I was the only one to be with him for those times. I protected him from intrusions. Toward the end, you see, Mr Buren was plagued by ideas of truth and recompense. He wrote his memoir to try and clear his head. He was a good man; but I always thought he carried a great weight. He spoke to me about these things. He felt he failed his brother. He felt he had wronged Mr Monroe. He felt that all his life he misplaced his energies. He was gifted with the most valuable commodity in human existence: time. He outlived everyone who meant anything to him. He was rich beyond reason. And yet he felt he had failed in everything because he had wasted his time."

It was a well-prepared, if odd, speech which Julius delivered with a round chest and a certain oratorical gravity.

On Buren's desk was a stack of charcoal drawings – a young woman's face, over and over again, from slightly different angles, but the same expression.

"Who is this?" I asked.

"I would imagine it is his brother's wife if you mean the drawings?" said Julius.

I looked through them all. A beautiful woman, she looked relaxed but serious, a labyrinthine glint to her eye, a downturn to the mouth, she was held up in a deeply-dug charcoal background.

Julius' intentions were grander and more central than he had first let on, I figured. Harold Buren was not just a former employer; Julius lived in his master's house, and had kept his study as a shrine even fifteen years after the old billionaire had died.

"This all seems a little like another project," I said.

"You don't know what that book is going to tell you about Mr Monroe," said Julius. "I took employment with Mr Buren in nineteen sixty five. I was the only staff member. He spent much of his time in this study. Toward the end I often came in at the sound of him talking, as if to someone, but I knew there was nobody with him. He talked to me often about his brother, and about Mr Monroe.

"One day, he returned home from a business trip – it would turn out to be his last trip, in fact; he stayed very much within these four walls after that – he told me that he was going to write a memoir, and that I must take each page and keep it safe, and safe from *him* so that he had no way of revising his memories and his thoughts. I always believed that he trusted me entirely, but that it was my blindness that he trusted, rather than my character. He wrote this for the sake of committing it to paper, I believe. It is there to explain and to teach lessons."

"Lessons? To whom?"

"That I do not know," said Julius. "He was careful to be vague about such notions."

"So why do you want me to see it now?"

Julius seemed to soften, his mouth gave up its punctiliousness, and he even allowed his hands to loosen from their dutiful tensions.

"I am old," he said. "Part of me also would like to know what is in it. Part of me would like to know the truth of the man I dedicated myself to. I suppose we all have these moments of redress late in life."

We came to an arrangement, Julius and I; and I returned to the house to spend my time examining the manuscript, to spend my time with the careful and strangely fresh hand-written memoirs of Harold Buren.

*

The words and testament of Harold Buren

FOR THOSE WHO COME AFTER

When I was a child I talked to dragons, and they told me all about the future.

There was a time when they wandered the countryside, graceful and prodigious, but by the time I was around they spent most of the time in the mountains across the veldt, only coming down when they had something to say, or I had something ask.

"You will have to keep an eye on things," they said.

They circled me. I was dust to them, with a muss of dirty blonde hair and my grey short-trousers.

"Don't worry about the great battles to come," said one of them.

"You just worry about the great silences between," said another.

I didn't know what they meant. But one does not answer back to dragons; that much my father told me. The creatures of myth are older than us all, he said. Before I was born he hung around my mother's neck a pendant, known as The Dragon's Eye, made from the first diamond he ever dug out of the ground. It was to remind us where we were from – from the earth, our wealth and our souls. It was to remind us of the importance of that thing we are all born from: *truth*.

I am here now at the other end of my life. And I'll tell you what I know about *truth*; and what I know about myth also. I will do it because, even though I have never known you, I love you. I want to tell you the things that I know; the things you should know.

I saw my century as something best forgotten. I worked hard to forget. As somebody once wrote, I concentrated on "inviting quicker the inevitable inconspicuousness of yesteryear". But, it seems, at the point of this welcomed oblivion I had to fight it off in order to remember once again. And the first thing I remembered was the dragons of my distant childhood. And then the pendant. Games and trinkets. Monsters and trinkets. Perhaps as good a title for a memoir as any.

What sparks this? The *great occasion*. Everybody who is lucky enough to experience one should take the time to document it. My great occasion was long awaited. And now I am here in my home – back from Spain and all those circles squared – I will make my document.

Remembering must involve unlearning what I know to be right. Forgetting, when intended, is the most difficult of tasks. A life of knowing, watching, listening to the birds of every colour sing; and I gave it up for the good of all. But now I need to remember. I need to remember for you. I need to remember for good. You are my redemption and my final punishment. But I bow to the knowledge that I must tell the story for those who come after. You are my centre point, my audience, my apostle-if-you-wish. It is you who are the meaning of it all.

A Dictionary of Hard Words
Alison Moore

It is mid week, out of season. In the playground near the on-site shop, Sally is on the swings. She is there with a boy she met in the amusements yesterday. When he told her his name, she didn't quite catch it. "What?" she said. He told her again and she sort of caught it but it was something foreign and she's not sure; she's been avoiding using his name ever since.

Instead of swinging, Sally is turning in circles, the chains twisting above her. Her new friend is not swinging either. His feet are flat on the ground.

"Which caravan's yours?" he asks.

"The noisy one," says Sally, indicating the one she means, although it's not necessary, they can both hear the argument loud and clear. The caravan Sally is staying in is halfway up the hill. In bed at night, she can feel the wind buffeting the caravan's exposed sides; she can hear a tree's bare branches scratching at the thin metal walls and the single-glazed windows.

Looking at what her friend is wearing, Sally says, "You've got your pyjamas on."

"It's not my pyjamas," he says. "It's a onesie."

"My dad says if he ever sees a dictionary with the word 'onesie' in it, he'll tear the fucking page out. He hates it when they let new words in the dictionary. It like literally makes him explode." She lifts her feet off the ground and the chains untwist, spinning her in jerky circles.

He shrugs. "There'll always be new words," he says. "The language has to change. There used to be dictionaries of words we'd got from other languages like Latin and Greek and French, words that people didn't know what they meant. I saw one in a museum: *A Table Alphabeticall of Hard Words*."

When Sally thinks of hard words, she thinks of the words that get used in fights, words that come out of nowhere and have nasty clusters like 'tch' and 'nt' and 'ck', and their vowels that are not the ones that make an 'aa' or 'ee' or 'oo' sound, like someone getting something nice; the vowels are 'i', dots and dashes like morse code, and 'u' which makes a sound – *uh* – like someone getting sucker-punched in the guts. Her dad sings a lot – when he's in the bath, when he's getting dressed, when he's cooking; you can always tell where he is – and one of the songs he sings is called 'Sorry Seems To Be The Hardest Word', but sorry is not the hardest word; the hardest words are those said through clenched teeth, through slammed-shut doors.

"They're everyday words now, though," says her friend. "They're just part of our language."

He lifts his feet and starts to swing, and then Sally starts to swing as well, the two of them kicking their legs out to get themselves higher; their toes, and the chains that hold them to the rusting frame, reaching out towards the pale sun.

Mikhail Omar Latas – II
Chris Cornwell

Omar,
thinking,
As nuts tinkle on the ceramic
and roll;
As you rifle slowly round and round, listlessly,
limp-wristedly
washing your hand in a bowl of rumbling fruit
Your rings clinking
in the windowsill, sat waiting
for the regeneration of trenches.

Did ever you eat the bowl
of cherries and rose petals and pears,
Pasha?
Did those fruit ever seem unwilling
or was their juiciness alone enough to consent?
Did you peel the skin from the fruit like
The Zlata, the sainted,
Pasha?
Out in exile Pasha,

exile.
But did you also smell the scent of almonds
Within the attar,
The cyanide scent of almonds
The suicidal aroma?
Did ever it ask you who you were? Where you were
born.

Was there a maiden missing some flesh
already hanging from the bows of the tree,
when you arrived,
pear blossoms on her shoulders.

Behind the hill in the blood gutters; the
groves of roses
Shadows leaning ever forward
Your men sniff with superannuated nares
The warm evening musk;
Suleiman The Old Leer of Europe
with the odour of the valley in his sinus
and the pollen of the damask staining his nose
Took the spoon to his lips at sunset.

Was the sent enticing
Or exciting?

Wash the black water from you sword
Pasha
with the otto of rose
And wipe the water from the blade
Over the dry earth,
over the blooms
In Bulgaria.

The Way
Jamie Guiney

You place a hand inside each boot and are thankful they are dry. You lace them up and take a moment to stretch both calves, before slinging on your red rucksack and stepping out into the fresh morning with its faded stars and pink sky. You pause to take in the beginnings of a new day, and still, the sun has not yet risen, nor the moon left the sky.

Before long you find the path flowing underfoot like a dry riverbed and you think about all of those who have walked this ancient way. You know by now that it is more than a path, yet still just a path, because it can change from hour to hour, and from day to day.

You tread and breathe, one foot then the other, and notice the awakening sky, its slow yawn into pastel blue, its broad halo of orange and yellow. Out in front, the long shadow of your body stretches along the stony track and you look two storeys tall. Your breath becomes a comforting rhythm and it surprises you how much contentment can be found just from breathing.

The barley fields that run either side of the path, interchange from unripened greens, to golden lakes, to pale fields of almost white. By the time the sun is strong against the back of your neck, your shadow has shortened and the path edges become lined with yellow flowers, twisting their way out through the corn like firecrackers.

You sometimes hear birds in the trees, their flutter of song or rhythmic calls, and if you are lucky, catch a glimpse of them in their temporary perches. The path widens as you pass through something that barely resembles a settlement - a handful of houses with grapevines creeping their porches, a faded sign hung against a plain stone wall where you enter into a bar to rest a little and enjoy some coffee, a soft fresh croissant.

When you leave, the sky is rich beyond comprehension, deep and cobalt, simple yet luxurious. As you journey further, cornfields become tall grass and yellow flowers are complemented now and then with white daisies whose petals have waned overnight and only just begun to look for the sun.

You see a figure in the distance, sitting by the side of the path and as you pass you can see the lethargy in his face, the sweat in his hair. On the path he is not a banker or a builder, he doesn't work in an office or paint pictures by the sea – he is just a human. You reach into your rucksack and give him a paraguayo and a smile and wish him 'Buen Camino' and he responds with a nod.

You continue to walk, it has become the melody of your life. You approach hills that are long and steady and as you rise up through their dry beaten paths, the fields fence in large cream cows who stand watching you in unison with their beautiful horns and the clink-clink of the metal bells around their necks. For the next while you hear the peppered sounds of their chimes until you pass a forest down in a valley with a warm wind moving gently through its foliage and the symphonic sound of bells coming back to you from animals you cannot see – so you laugh and christen it the musical forest.

You come across a man treading slowly with a staff and although you both speak different languages, you try to communicate anyway and you both laugh at the incredulity of it, the humanity of it, leaving each other with a smile and a handshake and a 'Buen Camino'.

You see now that the people are the path, that their souls are linked to yours.

The sun is stronger now, guiding you from behind, helping you on. Along the dishevelled edges of the track, start to spring up tall poppies that multiply as you walk until you are bordered with wonderful crimson richness, spreading out into a red sea of beauty all around. You smell faint perfume and all at once, the flowers are in you, part of you and part of the universe at the same time.

You think about the man with the paraguayo, how tired he was, whether he found enough strength to keep going, and then you pause on the track, in the hot afternoon, to catch a breath, to take a drink of water. It is time to sit, so you take off your rucksack for a few minutes and eat some bread, some chorizo. There is a silence that encourages your being.

When you set off again, the rucksack feels heavier and you know you are waning, that the day is wearing itself out. You follow a tree-lined path and there, as though hiding from the world, is a small church that you enter for nothing more than a look around and some welcome shade. Perspiration trickles your brow, you wipe it away and place both hands against the cold stone. There is no-one around and after cooling a little, you leave.

The sun is high and bright now, your legs beginning to tire. You glance towards fields that are vast and endless, the path winding through them like a slung rope. Out in the barley, you catch the flicker of a giant stork lifting off into the air, you witness the majesty of its spread wings and it is then that you know you have seen God, that you have seen him in everything your eyes have fallen upon since you stepped outside this morning.

As the afternoon fades and aches settle into your bones, you see a huddle of roofs in the distance and know this is where you will stop for the night. You know that even though the day has been long and filled with your own dusty footsteps, you have felt calmness and peace that no person will ever know unless they too venture out here where the wild poppies grow.

Dazzling the Gods
Tom Vowler

Even the bluebottles have succumbed. Half a dozen, upended
on the window sill, legs sculling the air in attempts to right
themselves. The room a kiln, sun livid as it seethes onto the
glass, braising him in a broth of wretchedness. People
comparing it to a time before all this, when there were
standpipes in the road and you could cook an egg on the kerb.

Sitting up in bed he eyes the net curtain for hints of a
breeze, some portent today will be cooler. Their sheets reek
again, despite his having washed them yesterday, and he
unfurls them from the window where they hang in limp
surrender. In the kitchen he fills a glass with ice and water.

Electra left the flat before he woke; hopefully the heat
or a need for food drove her out so early, and not another
capitulation. As far as he knows she's been clean for a month;
still some way short of his own effort, but a start all the same.
He'd stuck with her each time she caved to the tyranny of
cravings, every setback hardening his resolve. Strangely, he
found withdrawal, if not easy, then manageable once those
first hellish days were negotiated, although he knows such

dependence reaches into the marrow and never entirely recedes.

Looking around he estimates a single car-load will do: clothes, scores of tools, a bureau that had been his grandfather's. Where uncertainty exists over ownership, or they acquired something together, he will leave it behind, an act born of guilt or kindness, he is unsure. Her absence this morning has given him the option of cowardice, his farewell scrawled rather than spoken. The kind of letter you write when the mix becomes one part love, two parts loathing. Perhaps she already senses his departure and has chosen not to witness it, preferring a silent cleaving.

He downs the water, rolls the glass across his forehead. Already the floor pulses to the music below, incessant base that will reach deep into the weekend. He turns the radio on, a politician and scientist blaming each other, arguing about the figures, the tipping point. Outside the city groans and withers and looks skyward for relief.

She struck him last night. Something between a slap and a punch to the side of the head.

- It's the heat, she said later, stroking the mark to his face. We need to get out of this place.

Even then, despite what the drug had taken from her, he thought her beautiful, hoped some essence of it might be salvaged, nightfall affording sufficient respite. But when sleep came it brought only images of the baby.

He thinks about washing up last night's plates. It's an exaggeration to term the flat squalid, but it has long ceased being homely, their upkeep sufficient only for a life of sorts. After getting clean he found work at a scrapyard, welding skips four days a week, cash in hand. The men there, perhaps mindful of a rapid turnover, keep to themselves, sharing nothing but muted cigarette breaks with him. The only ones to converse are the Romanians, eager to practice newly-learnt phrases on him or to discuss the politics of their country. From what he understands, more than anything they miss a food called *sarmale*, a type of stuffed cabbage best enjoyed with smoked meat and sour cream. That and țuică, a strong spirit made from plums and sold in markets or by the roadside in unmarked bottles. The youngest showed him a family photo once, wife and new-born, told him he was welcome to visit anytime he was in Eastern Europe. When your own country is underwater, he joked.

Since the latest heatwave, the owner of the yard allows them to start at 5am – it's bad for business having workers die – and they finish around midday, when he comes home and collapses half-dead in a cold shower, his body brutalised yet purged some more. Electra would still be in bed, her logic that shorter days narrow temptation's window. When she did get up, a frisson of energy flashed through her and she'd reel off extravagant plans for their escape, to live in the country, clean and healthy, to start over. They would keep hens, make ginger beer.

- Everyone should be able to see the horizon, she liked to say. Everyone should hear birdsong.

Such manic bouts burned themselves out by evening, replaced with uneasy silence, with sleepless nights where she'd wail and thrash and spit and blame him for their purgatory. It was true he introduced her to heroin, a week or so after they met, when smoking it had been enough.

- It'll be OK, he'd whisper, trying to hold her, and she'd tell him to say something that wasn't a lie.

In the beginning, when their bodies took hungrily from each other, her tongue hot in his mouth, his dreams laced with her, it never occurred to him to keep something back, to shore up that part of the self too brittle to expose.

He watches the cars below snarl and stammer nowhere, white light blazing off their roofs, dazzling the gods. Sirens start up to the south, like dogs prompting one another. Last week the young Romanian was sent home with suspected retina burn, a weld flash from someone's gun as he removed his helmet prematurely. They knew not to go to the hospital, but to bathe the eyes in milk or use a saline solution until someone came round, a doctor of sorts. Two days off, they were allowed, unpaid, and if a fuss was made, someone else, not a doctor of sorts, came round. The pain, he knew from his days as an apprentice, would arrive in the night, like hot sand rubbed hard into the cornea. You might as well stare at the sun.

He makes a strong coffee and listens to the couple next door argue. The side of his face still smarts a little, a hotness overlying the ambient heat. He never retaliated, hadn't even raised his voice when she continued using. It was the perfect reason to stop, of course, for only the most selfish and cruel junkie continued poisoning a body that encased another.

He rolls a cigarette, listens to the soft sizzle as he draws on it. There'll be financial contrails to his leaving, some of which he hopes the envelope of cash will remedy. He'll pay the rent for a month or two, until she sorts something.

He fills a couple of bin sacks with clothes, sweating with the exertion. At the back of a drawer he finds a toddler's bodysuit, neatly folded with tags intact. A gift from a neighbour, it escaped Electra's cull when, unable to give everything up, he'd hidden it there. He brings the fabric to his face, inhales its scent, but it's just his own. He'll visit the hospital later. There's a memorial garden in its grounds, an entire plot devoted to the premature, where they'd taken flowers a couple of times soon after and again on the anniversary, until even this lapsed to neglect.

When you befriend heroin, you begin a slow and steady walk towards a rotating buzz-saw. Whether or not you can deviate from this trail long enough to escape its gravitational pull depends on several factors: your genes and personality; the number of dopamine receptors in your brain; the drug's availability and your exposure to those who use it; the presence of a mental disorder; physical or sexual abuse suffered early in life. Addiction to opiates is rarely immediate; numerous tributaries offer themselves as exit routes but their number diminishes with each hit. Bizarrely, most people will experience heroin at some point in their lives, usually in the moments before death, when it's administered as morphine to ease the passage. Frequent users are forced to search for novel routes to the bloodstream as veins collapse. Alternating sites can prevent this, moving from inside the elbow, down the forearm – avoiding arteries, making sure vessels don't have a pulse – into the back of the hand or the palm if the pain can be tolerated, into the fingers. Stomach, groin, thigh, calf and feet are all feasible. Neck, breasts, face and genitalia all carry increased risk but offer a last resort when you've spent hours stabbing away at flesh. During his most prolific period as a junkie, he knew someone who once injected into her eye.

 - Stay squeamish, was her advice.

He places his tools in a plastic crate taken from the yard, leaving spares of those duplicated, enough for her to carry out rudimentary tasks. The landlord works on the principle of not bothering you if you didn't bother him, so tenants tended to make their own maintenance arrangements.

He will miss the flat, its allusion to a status of sorts. Thirty-five. Halfway along life's path and almost nothing to show. What had been his lot before it was reduced to suspended animation? Memories surface when he allows: helping his brother build the landscaping business; being rubbish in goal and laughing in the pub afterwards. Of everything it laid claim to, perhaps friendship was the keenest loss.

From the kitchen he hears the flat door open and close. He calls out her name, but by the time he emerges to explain the bin sacks, she has shut herself in the bedroom. Perhaps the shoplifting has resumed, the impulse to take what was not hers gaining new purchase. It occurs to him just to leave, the words he will utter gratuitous, the worst cliché. Why wound each other further? Better to retain a semblance of respect.

Her crying sounds theatrical, strident bursts that are more felt than heard. He finds her crouched beside the bed, the noise – not hers, he now sees – settling to a steady whimper, as if the heat forbade such effort. The baby's face radiates from a circled opening in the towel as Electra rocks it back and forth in an easy cadence. Small runnels form above its nose in a half-frown, its eyes blinking before fixing on nothing in particular. The thrum of music from below, coupled with the motion, appears to soothe the child, its bawling finally receding to nothing. Electra reconfigures the towel in order to place a finger in the baby's hand, which after a second or two it grips.

So this is a mirage, he thinks – the sun orchestrating some divine revenge, a punishment befitting their crime. A glimpse at the unrealised. He says her name but she won't look at him.

- What have you done?

She raises a hand to indicate the need for quiet, her febrile smile traversed by a single tear, her forearm blazed with the blistered track-marks that resemble one of the great constellations. He kneels down, careful not to get too close.

- Electra, where did you take it from?

She cradles the bundle, humming softly now, his presence incidental. Leaning back he draws the curtain to keep the sun from them, the baby threatening to cry at the noise, before attending again to Electra's serenade. *If that mockingbird won't sing…*

He speaks more softly this time, placing a hand on her leg.

- We have to return it. I can take it back.

She ignores him so he tries a different approach.

- It's too hot in here.

He holds his arms out and she shifts back like some wild and frightened thing, tightening her grip. If there is any separating the two of them, it will not, he realises, happen without violence.

He supposes the child is a day or two old, its eyes in awe of each new sensation, the beginnings of a smile forming, its new world settled enough now to be of comfort. It won't always be this hot, he wants to announce, keen to apologise for the previous generation's decadence. Watching this absurd version of motherhood play out he allows a fantasy to form, one where such unfathomable gifts go unquestioned. Perhaps the world is reordered now; perhaps things like this happen.

He stands and Electra shoots him a look, eyes aflame in maternal defiance.

- It needs something to drink, he says. Some milk or water.

His apparent collusion relaxes her a little.

- What shall we call her? Electra says.

In the kitchen he can hear more sirens and imagines the panic, the fretful scramble, wonders how someone can be so careless. This cigarette is harder to roll, his hands atremble, his body remembering a more potent remedy, one that begins in the poppy fields of Afghanistan and ends in such lavish misery. It was never really about the rush for him, the fabled fire that tore through his veins in euphoric rampage. More it was the sense of serenity, of being held, as if by a parent or lover, warm and cosseted, the day kept just enough at bay.

He looks out across the scorched city and thinks about the things people live for, the poison and love they depend on.

He thinks about the young Romanian, how he'll keep his helmet on those extra few seconds now if he wants to see his child again. And he thinks about the call he will soon make, that will lure the sirens to them, that will make her hate him even more, perhaps forever. He will give her a few more minutes, though; he owes her that

Two Poems
Caitlin Thomson

DEER

My grandmother found a doe
besides her chicken wire fence,
its neck snapped. She called for
removal, but no one would take it.

She got into her tractor, and shoved
the deer to the edge of the highway.
She called animal control
to report a doe hit by a car.
It was gone within the day.

This happened right before her eightieth
birthday, that is the part of the story
I was always intrigued by.

Yesterday before breakfast I walked
a half mile to the view of the bay.

While gazing down at the oysters
in their neat rows, the net over the
clams twice the size of a football
field, a smell overwhelmed,

the sweet rot of it. On the way
down I saw it, a fawn the size
of my dog, lying by the side of the
path. Since then I have smelled it,
felt it in my throat, even in the shower.

I picture my grandmother differently.
Now, her mouth is covered with a mask,
her hands are clad in yellow gloves, even though
she doesn't touch it. When I return

the next day the smell is no longer
there, the body is shriveled and black
like the body of a child from
Pompeii caught in the ash.

THE GUTS

My mother told me that I always had a knack for danger,
over a glass of wine. She told me a story I had forgotten.

A stranger in a circle, of kicking and punches in second grade,
How I had gone in to get her out, but no one had retrieved me.

The principle had called my mother afterwards.
I had tripped in the school yard, someone

had helped me up. I limped for weeks.
Had a black eye I don't remember. I went back the next day.

I thought of the things my mother didn't know about second
grade, the time I was locked in the washroom, the time

that was worse than that. I let my mother share her
memory,
the way she screamed at the principle. I left it at that.

Pulse

Valerie Sirr

Your Dad's fingers tapped the armrest of his plastic chair. He kept perfect time. You knew because your hand was resting on his. His feet tapped on the sandy floor and yours swung in mid-air. You had to stop every so often because the rim of your seat dug into the backs of your thighs, but you could not stay still for long. *Dad said it was celebration music,* you wrote in your diary later.

It was raining hard outside, belting onto the sloping roof of the big tent, flowing in grey rivers down its sides. The wind almost drowned the music in the quiet parts, then the man with the trumpet stood up and the white-faced drummer made thunder noises as if fighting the storm outside.

You looked at the people in the rows in front of you. Some had smiles on their faces and their fingers tapped on elbows and knees. A thin-faced man with a down-turned mouth sat very still with his head cocked to one side on his long neck as if waiting for the music to be poured into him. Some people had their eyes closed while their heads nodded to the beat and their ankles swung in circles. Wind blustered outside and the music lifted and fell inside the swelling white walls. Across the rows fingers and feet and foreheads bobbed, as if the pressure built up inside people and escaped through the edges of them and in the steam from their damp coats.

The music ended with an explosion of drums. You both moved outside with the crowd. Your Dad was humming to himself still, and whenever the crowd stopped, you both did a bit of your Strictly Come Dancing waltz.

He said, 'Come on, Jess. One-two-three. One-two-three.'

You stood on his shoes so you could learn the rhythm.

Some of the mothers were watching. When you were out together women often stared. They would chat with your Dad and they would pat your head and lift your chin with their soft fingers. They would say 'spitting image' and 'the spit of you' and you would wonder what spit had to do with anything. Spit was what your granny put on her hanky to rub ice cream off your mouth. Your mother said 'Ewww,' when she did that and it smelled as sharp as your mother's face. The chatty women had happy faces. They had bright smiles and you liked it when they kissed you. They smelled of fruity lip-gloss and they stickied your cheeks with their lips. Your mother didn't wear lip-gloss. Your mother said lip-gloss was for women who were asking to be kissed. Your favourite kisses were from your Dad. Morning ones were best. You would rub noses and he smelled of toothpaste and his face wasn't scratchy like later.

He would say, 'Missing you already!' and you would
laugh, then you would count the cracks his knees made going
down the stairs. Sometimes you would count the seconds in
between the cracks. At night-time he skipped steps when he
came in from work, so there were less cracks to count. You
would sit up in bed and you would do your hug. He would
hold you against him and you would listen to the rhythm of
his heart. You would stay like that until your mother shouted
'Paul!' from the bottom of the stairs. *Our hearts have the exact
same rhythm,* you wrote.

When you got back to the car your mother was asleep. She
went for sleeps in the afternoons because there was another
baby coming. You hoped it would be a boy. Your mother
hoped it would be a boy too.

One day she was hanging shirts in the wardrobe and
your Dad was sitting on the bed loosening his tie from his
neck. Their door was half-open. You were on the landing
doing homework. There was a place on the landing in front of
the hot press where you could hear everything in your house.
Even if it was quiet, you could hear hums and creaks and
clicks and the gurgles in the attic from the tank. You heard
your mother telling your Dad about Emily Dunne and the race
on the way to school. That you were winning so Emily tripped
you up. You remembered the gravel scraping bits off your
knees and when you got up your blood was drumming in

your ears as if your head was going to burst and you thumped Emily Dunne until she screamed. You heard its high pitch for ages afterwards and your blood was buzzing as if somebody had plugged you in. *My mother said a boy might be easier, could hardly be any worse,* you wrote.

'Do you hear me, Paul,' your mother's voice had reached up from the bright hall. 'Are you listening?'

You looked down through the banister rods. Your Dad gave a loud sigh then your mother made a stiff little nod and went towards the kitchen. You saw the side of your Dad's face in the mirror. He was opening his top button. He was smiling.

Your mother woke with a jump when you banged the car door shut. She sat up straight, blinking, while she pulled herself out of her dream. Your Dad started up the engine and the windscreen wipers went whoosh, slap! whoosh, slap! Then the indicator started its click-click, click-click and you kicked your feet against the back of your mother's seat until she said, 'calm down, Jessica!'

Later you all had pizza in the sitting room. You sat at the coffee table drawing one of your designs. The voice of a newsreader vibrated in your ears. Your mother yawned. The wind in the chimney made a shriek and blew smoke out into the room. The weather girl on the TV screen pointed at clouds and flashes of lightning. On nights like that you would imagine you were all in a horror film, being attacked by the spirits outside.

You looked at your mother and Dad. They were listening to an opera documentary. Sometimes you got a feeling between them. It was like the tingle you got on your skin when your friend touched your arm after rubbing the sole of her shoe against the nylon carpet in her room. You decided not to move onto the couch because your mother's legs were in your place now and her feet were on your Dad's lap.

'He's a tenor,' you said.

The singer's chest was lifting like somebody was blowing him up. You looked at your Dad but his eyes were closed. Sometimes music closed his eyes and other times it made them watery. You went back to your drawing. The tenor's voice was rising as if he was going to cry. You moved your hand across your page pushing your pencil down, then up again to a peak. The orchestra music got louder then broke into a shower of sounds, like when the Halloween bonfire on the green shatters the air with flying blue sparks. Your mother sat up and turned the volume down.

When your Dad stood up from the couch he had a funny look on his face. You thought he was doing his clown impression. Sometimes he did that to make you laugh like Happy Face, Sad Face and Scary Face at Duffy's circus the year before, pushing their noses right up to you where you sat in the front row, shouting at you: *HAPPY! SCARY! SAD! SAD!*

SCARY! HAPPY! You wrote that in your diary in your best capital letters. You used to wonder which one would shout next and you would both laugh until you got pains in your stomachs and nearly fell off your seats.

You went back to your drawing again. The wind in the chimney was bellowing and beating against the walls. You imagined the big tent flying and trees keeling over outside. You pushed your pencil along the page, making a long blue zigzag line, but your Dad's plate fell onto the carpet and a splash of orangey tomato sauce blotted everything out.

'Paul?' your mother said. Her voice sounded like Violet in *Lemony Snicket* when she was scared but being brave.

Your Dad was leaning against your new keyboard. His hands pressed down on the lid. His eyes were squeezed tight. There was shiny sweat on his forehead. His lips were drawn back like Scary Face and you could see him clenching his teeth.

'My phone's in the car!' your mother said. She ran to the front door.

An icy draught wound itself around you, mixed with your mother's shaky voice, speaking into her phone and your Dad's voice, slurring. You stood beside your Dad. You were shaking and all the warm air was escaping from the room. *Dad said every day had its bad bits, like the sad parts in a song,* you wrote later.

It was two in the morning but your aunt and your mother brought you because your mother said they should. You found the fourth floor. Trolleys were being pushed up the corridor. There was a blue blanket with holes in it on a man's legs, like the ones babies have in cots. He had a white thing on like a nightie and it was open all the way down his back. He had freckles on his shoulders.

He was your Dad.

The lights in the corridor were glaring and you could see the hairs on his chest standing out on end.

'Take it easy, Jessica.' Your mother knelt in front of you. Her face was white. Your tears had stopped by then, but your breath was fast and your insides were melting. The hospital noises got louder. You put your hands on your ears. Your aunt grabbed your arm. She pulled you along the corridor but you couldn't find the toilet so you had to get sick on the floor, then a nurse brought you all into a small room with grey chairs and charts where your mother sat and nodded at a very young doctor. He held the door open for all of you as he left. Your mother's cheeks were pinker now. You sat beside her and she pushed your hair out of your eyes and her voice felt as firm and cool as her leather glove against your forehead.

'Jessica, your father is fine. Your father is staying for a while. The doctor says–'

You repeated the words to yourself. Jessica-your-father-is-fine. Jessica-your-father-is-fine. Your heart was slowing down now. Jessica-your-father-is-fine.

'Jessica,' your mother was saying.

'Jessica, are you alright?'

After a while you were all allowed to go into his room. There were three beds in there and a lot of different machines. A big white curtain swished across a rail and a skinny nurse in a blue cardigan came out. She gestured at you to come forward and she stood at the foot of the bed writing on the back of a clipboard. Your legs were wobbling but you walked to the side of the bed.

Your aunt said, 'Sure he doesn't want us at all – he only has eyes for Jessica.'

Your Dad was propped up on pillows. He had a plastic mask on. Steam hissed from its holes. You looked at his eyes and they calmed you down, warm and brown, like always.

'Isn't she a good-looking girl?' the nurse said. 'Just like her father.'

You told her you had the most handsome father of anybody in your class. She looked at your mother and winked. Your mother and your aunt bent to kiss him and when they nudged you into him he turned his eyes to heaven. You kissed his forehead and he held onto your hand. You sat on the bed and the others pulled up chairs. Your Dad couldn't talk yet but you knew what he would have said: how's Jess? Or: tell me all your news. There were grey stickers on him attaching wires to his skin.

'He's electric,' your mother said, and the nurse and your aunt laughed.

The nurse put a black armband on him and pumped air into it until you thought it was going to explode. She said she was checking the pressure inside your Dad. She told you the machine was mapping the beats of his heart. Bip-bip, bip-bip, bip-bip, it drew lines up and down the paper like joined-up music on a sheet. She showed you how to take his pulse by pressing your fingers on his wrist, then you all sat quietly for a while and you felt safe inside the curtains, following the sound of your Dad's heart in the pale white damp of the air. You took your aunt's pulse next, then you stretched across the bed and took hold of your mother's wrist. You pressed your two fingers against her fat blue veins.

You pressed harder, and harder, and harder, but you kept on missing the beat.

Samuel Bacht, 'Waiting for Gilgamesh'
Liam Cagney

> Des fonctionnaires, des écrivains : auteur, créateur,
> poète, cet homme n'a jamais existé!
> – Rimbaud

During the first few years I spent under Dublin's streetlights, enjoying the city's sins after moving down wet around the ears from Donegal, this being back in the mid-2000s when Dublin, from Portobello to Parnell Street, a 'shabby Babylon' of patched-up brickwork and slanted smiles, was as a ransacked dressing room for me and my friends to get decked out and wrecked in, among the different heads I'd bump into at this time around town – blue-eyed German singer-songwriters, pretentious Irish heroin-using Rastas, the odd Dub – one of the real and veritable 'characters' was Sam, this tall, red-headed half-German guy from Donegal who I met at UCD, where like me he was doing an Arts degree. Sam looked like a ginger Thurston Moore, played bass with gusto and had a mouth like a crossbow; and the two holiest things in the world for this Donegal Sam – more than playing in

Doran's with his band The Expelled, more than getting smashed on Guinness and Jameson in Whelan's with his girlfriend Lore, more than smoking a big joint and hitting the IMAX, more than giving out about Irish music – were wrapping his head around weird, esoteric literature, the weirder and more esoteric the better. And getting off his face, the more disfiguringly off his face the better. These twin joys of Sam's, esoteric books and drugs, amounted to a real vocation for him, and, naturally enough, like wayfarers at some moonless crossroads, they sometimes collided together in the venue of his person: more often than not, landing with my friends at two in the morning in some basement club. Cutting through the wide-eyed throng, there in the centre of the dancefloor I'd be greeted by Sam's lanky frame, sweaty cheekbones lit up by the strobe, skinny jaw clenched, swollen eyes flashing, body pulsing to the beat with a battered copy of *The Illuminatus! Trilogy* clasped in his big half-German hand; or else, in the maddeningly persistent daylight of the UCD library on a weekday afternoon, when all the other students, having finished for the day, were off in the student bar drinking and trading gossip, as I happened to file through one of the library's less-often-visited zones of academic enquiry I'd catch a glimpse of Sam's tangled mass sat cross-legged on the floor, a stone circle of books arrayed around him opened onto various stuff like the purple pontifications of Eliphas Lévi, the amphetamine ramblings of

Bob Dylan's *Tarantula*, or Piero Della Francesca's arcane Treatise on geometry in painting, beats blasting out of his headphones, eyes half-rolled into the back of his head, chewing the face off himself, fucked, scribbling biro notes furiously in a copybook that in his state he probably couldn't even see. These were Sam's two fundamental facts: at his core he had a dual nature; and at his surface those two sides were constantly 'duelling'.

Anyway, what I want to relate here is Sam's theory of Beckett.

Sam's full name, remarkably – accursedly – was Samuel Bacht. But as far as I could tell, this homonymous 'doubling' he represented of the Irish writer never seemed to bother Sam. Never seemed to, that is, till one afternoon in the park – the last time I saw Sam – when, with all the perverted brio of a flasher, Sam exposed me to his theory of Beckett.

We'd gone to Stephen's Green to smoke a couple of joints after a lecture earlier in the day on *Waiting for Godot*. Except for a few workmen in yellow vests and the odd jogger, the Green was empty, and we sat on a bench overhung by leafless branches opening onto a lake across whose surface ducks coasted.

"What'd you make of the lecture, then?" I asked, innocently, taking my hipflask out. "Well, I'll say this, Liam. I'm constantly surprised how nobody gets how ridiculously overrated Beckett is. Everyone in this country, and particularly those who never read him, hold Beckett up as one of our "greatest scriptural sons", a saint in our literary church. But when you actually read Beckett in an unbiased way he's ridiculously overrated. These experts in drivel shove on Beckett's head the laurel wreath of "the greatest prose stylist of the twentieth century", a writer who allegedly invented a writing all his own. These people aren't just ignorant, they're stupid, trading on dim memories in dimmer brains of having read *Waiting for Godot* once years ago and then imitating afterwards what they think they're supposed to say about it. Parrots, Liam!'

'Pirates?'

'No, *parrots!* Anyway, if they actually took the time to read Beckett again,' Sam said, 'to give him another look, they'd clearly see, since it's as bare as a nudist's backside, that Beckett's prose isn't just hoary and old-fashioned and out-of-date, it's completely decrepit – just like Beckett's own characters, like Krapp and company.'

Sam broke to lick a skin. I noticed his right corduroyed leg was trembling like mad.

'The fact that Beckett can't write in the natural tongue,' Sam went on, 'the fact that he can't write as we speak but instead has to indulge in pallid, pseudo-Shakespearean artifice, shows that his writing is completely unexperimental and just amounts to a throwing of "literary shapes" for the bourgeois Biedermeiers of the literary establishment, who lap that shit up.'

Sam turned and looked at me now directly under his red fringe.

'In real life, Liam, you never actually hear people talk as they do in Beckett's plays. Because real speech is vibrant, it vibrates like a huge guitar string, while this "literary" speech is death. Beckett speaks the language of the stage,' he went on, 'not the language of life. And since Beckett poos out this entirely false, fabricated language, it's actually very fitting that it's in the theatre that Beckett's revered more than anywhere else, where the whole premise is dress-up and glitter.'

A pensioner passing by with a Jack Russell on a leash cast us a furtive glance, Sam having lit up the joint.

'A few weeks ago,' Sam said, exhaling, 'Lore and myself went to the Project Arts Theatre to see the new Fiona Shaw production of *Happy Days*, with Fiona Shaw as Winnie. Fifty euro for two seats in the gods. Anyway, when the curtain went up the two of us were inundated by a pelt of words so totally unintelligible, so totally foreign to our ears that after only five minutes we literally had to throw on our coats and run out the exit. And it was such a relief to be outside afterwards in the cool air of Temple Bar. The relief you get after leaving mass. What you hear a character say in a Beckett play you would never hear a person say in real life.

What you hear in a Beckett play is always self-consciously 'literary' (Sam did the gesture for inverted commas) and about as close to real speech as an elephant is to a mandarin. Which goes to show, for those who can throw off the blinkers, that Beckett has had his day. And Beckett knew his writing was a linguistic disaster, which is why in his later dramatic works he gets rid of the speech altogether and just choreographs movement and gestures – out of guilt over what I call the *"grand swindle"*, the grand *"shrouded charade"* that is Beckett's plays' language.'

Now drops of rain were unsettling the surface of the lake. Getting up from the bench we started east along the perimeter of the park heading towards O'Donoghue's for a pint. As we walked under the lime-flanked avenue, Sam's freight-train-of-thought careered on.

'I'll give you an example. When Beckett describes, with his decrepit zest, the little green patch of grass – 'the little green circle amid an otherwise brown country' – that's probably the stupidest thing I've ever read.'

Sam's big boots sent out methodical thuds as we strode past the emaciated stone bodies of the famine monument, exiting the park. Dodging a bus, we crossed on to Merrion Row. The rain was coming down now heavier.

'Beckett insists, Liam, on drawing in our minds a vivid mental image of this little green circle, this little green patch of grass, 'the wild yet cultivated patch of grass' – then proceeds to do nothing with it but simply have us look at it as if we're a herd of depressed cattle. 'The little verdant circle, hemmed in with gorse, a little pastoral portal, gorse and greenery, bucolic bushes, streaming green, asphodels and daisies, flowers like yellow chewing gum blooming from Nature's pavement, birds invisible, inaudible, in this little verdant circle, this little green patch of grass,' as I think Beckett writes. 'No man. No night. No day. Goodbye.' The whole thing brought to life, Liam, and then neglected, can you believe it, as Beckett just throws down a full stop and moves on quite nonchalantly to write about something completely different. Abandoned! And in this way Beckett is one long oblique mournful pastoral. He turns Ireland's landscape into a Protestant funeral.'

We had now reached O'Donoghues. Sam stood us two pints of Guinness and we took a seat by the window.

'But Beckett's pen's black ink, anyway, completely poisons that fertile green. By writing it he signs the green circle's autopsy report. Beckett's toxic pen-ink renders the lush green grey and withered. The greenery, the green grass that Beckett also calls 'a lake of green grass' – how pretentious! The scratching of Beckett's pen kills it dead and it can literally never be green again, Liam. 'In the rustling of the whins, the fluttering of the reeds, a voice onwards stealing, oblivious, nothing saying, speechless, mute speech, brash silence.' Beckett kills this imaginary country, turns it into a show, like a stuffed animal.'

Sam nodded in assent to himself.

'Over time Beckett's memory will be not only tired but absolutely void. Beckett who so strikingly said, remember: 'I am dancing around the void. Dancing, I am, flailing with one foot in my hands, around the void.' Beckett's famous phrase. 'Around and round I go, around and round and round, around the void I go,' writes Beckett,' said Sam. 'Around the void, around the void like a vulture, swirling around and round, dancing around and round, a vulture of the void, a void's vulture,' writes Beckett,' said Sam.

Some of the men at the bar were now looking over at us, since the volume of Sam's voice had been steadily increasing.

'Beckett writes about dancing around the void, about going round the void like a vulture,' said Sam, quieter now. 'Well Beckett, soon you'll no longer be dancing around the void, soon you will *be* void, soon you will *become* the void, your enticing circular dance's aim will really succeed, your fake incantation will resonate in reality. And the little green patch of grass will disappear into nowhere.'

Sam supped at his pint.

'You know that *I'll* be remembered when Beckett's in oblivion. After the phony original's in the wastepaper bin.'

Sam took off his heavy purple army jacket and hung it over the radiator. I noticed he was wearing several rings.

'You know what *Waiting for Godot*'s about, though? It's about schizophrenia, about being schizophrenic. The reason the two main characters are essentially interchangeable is because Didi and Gogo are in fact one and the same man. One's projecting the other. A phantasm. And Godot obviously never comes because he's just a delusion. So what the audience sees isn't actually happening.'

I noticed the television in the corner was showing horse racing.

'I'll tell you, though, Liam,' Sam said, looking at me over the sunglasses he'd just put on, 'why do we need dead writers anyway? Isn't that antithetical to what writing's about? Fiction's supposed to be living, fiction's supposed to jump around on the page like a frog, a pair of amphibious eyes darting around here and there, manically, alarmingly, at times almost musically, swivelling to see what it's literally impossible for us ourselves to see. But Beckett's 'dead eyes' – and he wouldn't deny that epithet – show us only *deathly spectacles*. In Beckett's mordant pupils float mordant scenes only. *Deathly spectacles* – basically Beckett's whole life's work, sitting on our nation's bookshelves, is one long *deathly spectacle*, Liam. Whereas it should be a *live wiring*. Live wiring *must* replace the deathly spectacle. I say live wiring because our two staring eyes are live wires conducting a vital current between our brains and the world. Our vision, as I've said to you before Liam, is a sort of 'throwing'. We 'throw' our vision into the world, as if throwing a little rubber ball into a bucket. On the other hand, what we see is a 'catching', as if catching a baseball. The word *seen* really means 'caught', Liam, and the word *seeing* means 'throwing'. And the best way to remember all this is in terms of the bucket in the corner and the little rubber ball. But nowhere in life is there a deathly spectacle. *Deathly spectacle* is Beckett's sneakiest invention, in a career of nothing but sneaky inventions. *Deathly spectacle* animates the paltry inventory of Beckett's corpus. The phrase 'Beckett's life's work' actually means 'Beckett's deathly spectacle'. But Beckett's *work's life*, on the other hand, is what I call a 'fleeting scene', because soon it will fly away forever.' His diatribe finished, Sam now took a copy of the Sports section of the *Irish Times* someone had left behind on our table and he wrote with biro in big letters across it: 'DEATHLY SPECTACLE'.

Over the course of our conversation Sam had been tearing up the Budweiser beermats on the table into little smithereens of coloured card. Now he started arranging them. I tried to move the subject on.

'The Dubliners used to play here, didn't they? The band, I mean – I don't think O'Donoghue's is in *Dubliners*....'

'Well, for me, anyway, the strangest thing about Beckett now,' Sam replied, 'the biggest irony if you like, is that while Beckett's work is, as I've said, the mundanest of the mundane – read at school, cheap and meaningless, institutionalised – Beckett as a real person has become utterly *un*-mundane – the opposite. He was a worldly man in life, they say, but in death Beckett has become unutterably *un*-mundane. Beckett's corpus is now *mundane* while Beckett's person is now *un*-mundane. And it was the other way round while Beckett was alive.'

We'd reached the end of our pints so I took the opportunity to get up and go to the bar and order two more. Looking out the window as I waited, I saw it was lashing down outside. When I got back to the table Sam was hunched over sending a text, still wearing his sunglasses.

'So what was I saying… oh yeah. I'll tell you exactly what I mean, then, by mundane and *un*-mundane. Over the last pint, Liam, we established that Beckett's language was once considered the literary equivalent of snorting a line of China White, whereas if you look closely you actually see that it's self-consciously 'literary' in the most facile and unimaginative way this side of, I don't know, any one of our 'big writers', who are basically a group of men having a pissing contest up against a wall.'

I interrupted with a *sláinte mór*. We clinked glasses, then Sam went on:

'And in spite of the ostensibly "strange" surface of Beckett's work, Liam, despite Beckett's 'odd characters' and 'unlikely scenes', Beckett's language reveals that this strangeness is really a sort of nakedly 'fake' strangeness. Because Beckett's language is actually the acme, the apex of worldly careerism. Hence it's completely 'mundane',' said Sam, pointing at me. 'And this is how, Liam,' Sam said, still pointing, 'Beckett's work – with its careerist words and its nakedly 'fake' strangeness – this is how it's actually the most mundane thing in the world. While at the same time, Beckett himself, the same Beckett who Lore and myself went to see last summer in Paris laid out under a black slab in Montparnasse – a miserable day – has metamorphosed into something *un*-mundane. Beckett's *unmundaneness* – and I'll describe what I mean by that in a minute – Beckett's *unmundaneness* is unique to Beckett alone.' Sam took a heroic gulp from his pint, then slammed it down. 'Beckett's *unmundaneness* isn't possible or achievable for anyone else other than Beckett. His *unmundaneness* is peculiar to Beckett. It's 'the bespoke jacket time's doorman gave him on the way out,' if you like. Beckett's life's *unmundaneness* is the absolute polar opposite of Beckett's writing's nakedly 'fake' strangeness.' Sam was arranging the shreds of beermat into a little pile in the table's centre. 'Beckett's *unmundaneness* stems from the dirty soil of Beckett's work, Liam, growing and growing to cover Beckett's skin, merging with Beckett's skin's wrinkled folds, merging like a flower with Beckett's face' – Sam took off his shades and looked me square in the eye –

'Beckett's lustrous face, Liam, Beckett's haunted lustrous face, Beckett's porcelain folds.'

The rain had stopped outside. Merrion Row was lit up the colour of snooker balls. Figures walked at a normal pace by the window. I started wondering how I'd get back to Rathgar with no money for the bus.

'But it's the video on YouTube I've been getting at, Liam. The video on YouTube,' Sam went on, 'that's what I've been getting at.'

He silently looked me in the eye for about ten seconds before continuing.

'Someone's uploaded onto YouTube this short video of Beckett being interviewed. Although it's in colour, Beckett's pale – a 'studied paleness', a classical paleness, the monochrome of the keyboard on a piano. So in this hotel room in Paris, somewhere near rue Saint Jacques, Beckett's watching the TV and every now and again looking over at a phone, as a director, who's flown over that day from America, plays a video to Beckett of one of Beckett's latest works,' said Sam, 'which this director, whose name I don't remember, has taken it upon himself to reshape into a television play, much to Beckett's clear disapproval. Anyway, Beckett's dressed dapperly as usual in a smart black suit. Over his eyes he alternately places and then removes a pair of spectacles. So there I am, Liam, sat in the sitting room in Harrington Street in the small hours, watching TV, nobody else up, coming across this frankly bizarre video of Beckett, my detested Beckett, on the internet, this voyeuristic video of Beckett, coming across it by chance, my detested Beckett in the intimacy of a hotel room, *and he himself is watching TV.* Like me, at the same time, but elsewhere. Anyway, the provenance of the video is for me suspicious (is he just an actor pretending to be Beckett?) because of the total paucity of video footage of Beckett while he was alive. There's only pictures, Liam,' Sam said, tossing the shreds of beermat from their pile. 'This video of Beckett on YouTube held me rapt and riveted while my brain tried to take stock of it, sitting in Harrington Street in the middle of the night. Something happened to me. And when I thought about it it showed me this. Beckett, as he is in the video towards the end of his life, is in every respect now *one of his own characters.* The identification between work and man is complete. It's unsettling. The hair, the face, the skin, the tall frame, the noble mien, the black suit, the flower hung in his lapel, the brown bowler hat hanging on a hook on the wall behind him, the mild, vital eyes (his *live wires*), the faint tendrils in Beckett's bloodshot eyes' corners, the south Dublin lilt in the words of his slowly, softly unfolding voice – all of these things, and even the way the scene is composed and Beckett is framed within the shot – the grainy shot of a camcorder. Every element *speaks.*'

I indulged him:

'What does it say?'

''Beckett', Liam. The scene says, 'Beckett'. It says, 'Beckett', Liam. 'Beckett'. Not verbally but visually. The word 'Beckett' becomes in this video the signature of both the *man* and the *corpus*. A visual signature. In this video the man actually becomes the corpus. There's no duality now, just some cracked oneness. The writer's 'auto-written'. Beckett 'is' one of his characters, without acting. Hence he's *unmundane* – he's unreal and weird. And that is what I meant by saying that Beckett's *unmundaneness* is peculiar to Beckett. How could it not be? So having earlier created this image in his life's work, Beckett takes leave of his life by becoming his work. And he does it through shooting this video, and through, as Frank said once, *absence*, through absence as '*the absence of absence*', the realest absence of all. Like *Stirrings Still*. But once you realise this, Liam, it's a virus, it invades you.'

The barman lifted our glasses. Time to go.

*   *   *

A couple of years later, when I was back visiting friends in Dublin for a weekend and we were out at the POD, I was outside having a smoke when at the other side of the smoking area, dressed in a one-piece harlequin outfit, I spotted Lore. I went over and said hello. She was working at Google now, she said, and partying at the weekends. I asked her how Sam was keeping. Lore rolled her big black eyes and gave a weak smile.

'Ah, Sam. We broke up ages ago. Sam moved to Paris.'

In Paris, she said, where he moved without knowing anyone, Sam had gotten a job as an English teacher. He'd been getting really into film around this time, she said, shooting film. And he'd gotten obsessed with making a film about Samuel Beckett. This film was supposed to be shot in the theatre where *Waiting for Godot* had first been put on (*En Attendant Godot*). 'Going back to his roots, Liamo... or lack of them.' The theatre in question, the Théâtre de Babylon, however, is long since shut, and a travel agent's stands in its place. But undeterred, Sam had contented himself with shooting his film in the auditorium of the nearby Théâtre Lucernaire, where he got a job as a cleaner and which he went to at night. This film, Lore said, is one long fixed shot of the unlit stage. The empty seats of the hall are in the foreground. The film lasts several hours. About three hours in, a green spotlight falls on the empty stage for a while. Then it disappears again. That's the only event.

'Sam calls it *Waiting for Gilgamesh*.'

She breathed out a stream of smoke.

'And he keeps remaking it. Over and over.'

Old Roffe
Nigel Jarrett

Dusk at the Ornskoldsvik Zoological Garden is accompanied not by exotic birdsong, the trumpeting of elephants or the baboon's high-pitched warning cry, but by silence.

If Evelina Bengtsson was not the first to notice this, she was certainly the only one to think it worth mentioning. Young and eccentric, Lagman calls her. At six o'clock, Evelina is responsible for closing the two gates when the last visitors have gone and before the guards have made a final check.

She is walking now, at twilight, around the outdoor section of the aviary. Detention and freedom are matters often raised by Evelina at break times. Lagman, who looks after the seals and smells of fish, even when he deputises at the turnstiles for the cashier, Mrs Karin Beckstrand, has advised Evelina to lower her voice when raising such issues. Lagman has mixed feelings about Evelina's eccentricity. In many ways she is the perfect companion he craves, in others he feels he could not match her eagerness. But he admits that she has a relationship with the primates that none of the others can match. She talks to Roffe, the old gorilla, and he seems to listen. But Roffe's days are numbered: he has been throwing stones and other small objects at visitors, and his fence has had to be raised.

As she strolls past a bamboo break, its leafy canes gently swaying, she can see Roffe imprisoned fifty yards to her left, sitting alone in that awkward way he has developed with age. In the gloaming, he is following her progress to the gates. He now has a stoop, which makes his arms and knuckles and their use as walking aids look clumsy. Evelina has noticed that he sits and stares at the ground more and more. She thinks he is meditating. About what? Lagman asked, immediately regretting the slight contempt that edged his question.

As she starts up the incline beside a flamingo pool littered with discarded drink cans and wrappers, Evelina can see Mrs Beckstrand in her booth of light up ahead. She wonders if the resentful Mrs Beckstrand alone epitomises the flaws of the Ornskoldsvik Zoological Garden more than old Roffe or the hush and stillness that settles on the place at nightfall like a curfew. The source of the cashier's bitterness is not known. Mrs Beckstrand continues her oblivious accounting, a cigarette between her teeth, its smoke stinging her eyes. She turns tearfully to acknowledge Evelina's arrival.

Mrs Beckstrand wears a stippled rubber cap on her right thumb as an aid to counting banknotes. A week ago, when the turnstiles had quietened for a while, she called to Evelina and waved her over. In place of her clipped pleasantries, she said, 'Evelina, I want to ask you something.'

Evelina planted her elbows outside the Perspex screen with its talk-through disc and propped her chin on her hands.

Mrs Beckstrand continued, 'Do you have any family, Evelina, anyone close?'

It was a strange question, Evelina thought, uttered as someone might who wanted to borrow something. 'Why do you ask?'

Mrs Beckstrand did not like her inquiries answered with a further question and said, 'Well, it's just that…oh, nothing. It doesn't matter.'

'No, I meant….'

'Honestly, it doesn't matter.' This said with peevish emphasis.

Mrs Beckstrand waved her hand rapidly in front of her face to delete the exchange, just as a crowd of schoolchildren were approaching the entrance. Evelina noticed that she also placed her hand over her mouth as someone would who was stifling a rare and embarrassing sob.

This time, Mrs Beckstrand is mouthing silently as she counts, so Evelina goes ahead and locks up. Mrs Beckstrand leaves at the bottom gate each night. Evelina closes that gate too, before everything is double-locked by Security. Mrs Beckstrand doesn't see Evelina hold out her arms and look around her, smiling knowingly at the absence of roars and cries.

Suddenly, Lagman appears from behind a hedge.

'I thought you'd gone,' Evelina says, startled.

He jerks his thumb towards the ticket-office and says, 'I'm waiting to see Mrs B. Spot of bother with her fancy man. She told me about it on the bus last night.'

Evelina cannot resist an image of Lagman waiting - 'skulking' presents itself - across the road in Fabriksgaten for Mrs Beckstrand to emerge after work. Lagman likes the movies and Evelina is half-expecting him to ask her out. Without looking at him, she says, 'Fancy man? What do you mean, 'fancy man'?'

Lagman says, 'Good god, Evvy. Don't you know anything? She's been with him for years. Smart fella, something to do with shipping. Works all hours and travels abroad. Anyway, he's gone - walked out, just like that.'

'Perhaps that's what she wanted to tell me the other day,' Evelina muses, out loud. 'She took me by surprise. Inside her booth. I was wary.'

Lagman looks confused.

'You know,' she adds. 'Like something in a cage, changing its tack, trying to deceive you.'

Lagman continues on his way, waving without looking at her.

Sometimes on her evening circuit in winter, the silence, or her perception of it, has for Evelina a minatory character, as though the animals are ganging up. In this eerie atmosphere she wonders if Mrs Beckstrand has contributed to her estrangement, or has done something to cause it (or not done something that would have prevented it). Poor Mrs Beckstrand: her lover has flown.

Evelina looks back and sees Lagman standing in silhouette ten yards from Mrs Beckstrand's booth. He does not move. His gaze is fixed on the woman wrapping cylinders of notes in elastic bands (not many these days, to be sure), blinded in one eye by cigarette smoke. He knows Mrs Beckstrand cannot see him while she is drowned in her pool of light. Then he is inside the booth and they are arguing: at least, their faces are close together and Lagman's arms are outspread. Evelina wonders if Lagman is telling Mrs Beckstrand to pull herself together, or if he has made an ill-judged attempt to replace the 'fancy man' in her affections.

Minutes later, Evelina is standing by a bench, watching old Roffe. Then she hears footsteps. It is Mrs Beckstrand, on her way home.

'So Halvar has told you.' the cashier says, coming to a stop.

Mrs Beckstrand is always dressed smartly. Evelina is reminded of someone who can be easily transformed into a beauty, despite age. Under Mrs Beckstrand's arm is a scuffed leather briefcase.

'I'm sorry, Mrs Beckstrand. I really am.'

'Ah well. These things happen.' She is clutching the briefcase to her breast as possession, comfort, shield. 'Evelina, do you mind if I say something?'

Evelina senses what is coming.

'Don't discourage him,' Mrs Beckstrand says. 'Halvar. He's a shy one really. Give him hope. You two are of a mind when it comes to animals. And he is a looker, you know.'

The advice-seeker offers advice! Evelina understands. Lagman's arm-waving was despair (*Can't you have a word with her, Karin?* he probably said. *I think she'll refuse me. I don't want her to worry herself about having to say no.*)

'I'll see,' Evelina says, mystified, with a non-committal look sideways.

Mrs Beckstrand sniffs heavily, an act of relief, finality. If she has shed tears, there will be no more. 'Goodnight, Evelina,' she says. 'Remember what I said.'

Evelina watches Mrs Beckstrand step elegantly through the door built into the heavy main gate. She imagines her at the kerb, waiting to cross busy Fabriksgaten. For some reason she also thinks of a man on the deck of a ship pulling away from shore in the moonlight, a man with a new destination, the wind in his hair.

Old Roffe displaces her interest in these human foibles. She walks slowly towards his compound in the half-light. She treads softly and seats herself on another bench, half in shadow, and watches him. Something he does makes her slide further along the bench, out of sight beneath a willow's overhang. There is a sudden pounding in her chest. She thinks Roffe must hear it and detect her presence. But Roffe is absorbed in something new, something she has never seen before. He is picking up objects, as he often does, and after sniffing them and discarding what he doesn't need, he is holding them in his hand. Each time he does so, he looks over his shoulder, as if to make sure he is not being watched. She then realises that what he throws away is edible. He is smelling to reject the tasty and soft-centred. She sits forward, intrigued, for she believes that what Roffe is grasping in his hand, retaining, might be missiles, the bits and bobs that land on the path in daytime to the amusement of onlookers, some of whom toss them back, a practice abhorred by the Ornskoldsvik management. And he is seeking not reproachful interlopers but victims, the act a reflex of another one that has taken him, taken his brain, by surprise and confounded its usual implication. *He is collecting!*

Roffe then begins moving about in his painful way, the objects still in his hand. Then Evelina hears someone knocking at the side door. The security man on his rounds hears it too. Evelina watches. Mrs Beckstrand has returned. She has her back to Evelina. She sounds hysterical.

As Evelina strains to hear what Mrs Beckstrand is saying, she is surprised by a voice behind her. It is Lagman again.

'Evvy,' he says, half-whispering.

'Halvar! What on earth are you playing at?'

He steps forward and sits down, nervously looking towards the bottom exit.

'I need to speak to you,' he says. 'Isn't that Mrs
Beckstrand…what is she doing?…I thought…'

'I thought you'd gone too.'

'I stayed behind, to speak…Oh God, she's coming this
way…to look for me…'

'Look for you? Why would she want to do that?'

'She's suddenly taken against me for some reason. I don't
know. I was supposed to meet her in Fabriksgaten…at the
Florestan…'

Evelina smiles at these odd subterfuges. Lagman excuses
himself, explaining that he is returning to their hut. Mrs
Beckstrand begins making her way towards them, up a gentle
slope. Seconds later, she passes in front of Evelina about ten
yards away, with stomp-like tread, head lowered. She is
breathless yet resolute. Thinking everything is to do with Mrs
Beckstrand's truncated love life, Evelina focuses once more on
old Roffe, who is moving around intermittently, like a levered
boulder.

Roffe now appears to have two fistfuls of small objects. He
squats and examines them. He wipes his nose with the back of
his wrist. He lumbers forward again, towards his play-place,
an area laid with bark chips and overhung with ropes attached
to tyres. Walking with difficulty and pain, he suddenly stops
before a large stone and drops the objects he is holding in his
left hand. One hand thus freed, he lifts the stone and secretes
beneath it the contents of his right hand, followed by the rest

of his collection, allowing the stone to fall carefully - there is no other word - into place. Evelina jumps to her feet and strides into the open. Her heart, her imprisoned heart, is banging about inside her ribcage. She looks about her, seeking the perpetrator of this illusion, this trick played on a lone, unsuspecting woman. *He is saving them up!* she says to herself. *He is storing his ammunition for tomorrow!*

But other voices displace her phantom exclamations. Old Roffe hears them too. They belong to Lagman and Mrs Beckstrand, the lovers, who are coming towards her along the path. She makes no effort to hide again. Lagman is wearing his herring-bone overcoat (it always makes her chuckle) and his brown felt hat with its sierra band of sweat.

'You promised me you'd be there,' Mrs Beckstrand is saying.

'I had to speak…'

'Halvar Lagman, you are a coward. I waited. What were you thinking of?'

They pass Evelina, almost without noticing her. Mrs Beckstrand's head still droops, her breathing audible. Only Lagman takes an apologetic look over his shoulder. Evelina can see the security man fanning out the contents of his key-ring like a card sharp and wonders if she has it all wrong and that it is Mrs Beckstrand who desires the embraces of Lagman but is tempered by her recent loss into believing her instincts eternally ill-fated. It would explain a lot of things: Lagman's solicitude towards her (to make Mrs Beckstrand jealous enough to declare herself openly); Mrs Beckstrand's anger (at her divided self); the *contretemps* in the booth (Lagman imploring Mrs Beckstrand to make up her mind); Mrs Beckstrand's advice to Evelina to encourage Lagman's designs (an attempt to resolve matters in her distraught and tragic favour); and then Lagman's staying behind to speak (wanting her, Evelina's, advice, another woman's advice, about how to respond to fickle romance). As she thinks about these possible explanations, watching Lagman and Mrs Beckstrand step through the little door on to Fabriksgaten, something lands at her feet, bouncing once. It is a small pebble. She picks it up and squeezes it in her palm. In the distance, Roffe stares at her from millennia past, his eyes blinking.

*

These events took place in the Autumn, just before leaf-fall. By the following Spring, Mrs Beckstrand was dead: cancer of the lung with secondaries. The business with Lagman had been sorted. He'd been taking money from the till over a long period while deputising for her, as she suspected, but her leniency and tact had been extended to the moment of his confession, and he gave in his notice.

The evening Mrs Beckstrand waited in the Café Florestan to confront Lagman after work and talk about his fall from grace was when she knew there was something wrong with her. It wasn't just that she'd been left on her own or that she'd repaid some money herself and buried the other losses in the accounts. The embarrassment of having to cross Fabriksgaten, ring the security bell, knock the door in desperation when no-one came and walk past that delinquent old gorilla to have it out with Lagman made her overwhelmingly tired. If only Evelina Bengtsson had not left so soon after Lagman. Evelina - so many questions she even answered you with one; innocent Evelina, as yet without insight or knowledge, but the perfect antidote to Lagman's foolishness and a potential foil to its slide into cupidity. She tried to bring them together but none of her strategies had worked. Evelina left after the stupid gorilla was put down - because of old age, its internal agonies and its outer manifestations of the unacceptable. Lagman always said Evelina had a way with Roffe, whatever that had meant. They've all gone; but the Ornskoldsvik Zoological Garden still struggles along without them.

Two Poems
Steph Power

A - Z

Lines on a map, the city grid laid
bare in red-green patterns of
change, movement, order belying
chaos, the bumping together of
worlds within worlds.

A blueprint for lives lived in
journeys to the corner shop, a
conduit for need repeatedly
met or unmet.

Mile after mile, the street lamps
radiate anxiety, saturating
sleep with orange-yellow fog.
Here and there, muffled sounds
relocate the night. And through it
all the cunning foxes run.

MIX-TAPE

The man with the audiocassette
walked up the street and
into the steaming cafe.

In and out of pockets checking
cash, train ticket, cash,
train ticket, cash: the

time on the wall.

Open case, shut case,
open case, wind tape,
shut case.

Milky instant and a
plate of toast, eyes
blinking in the hot, fatty air.

Formica sounds for now, but a
private world in a
public space to measure the

time on the wall.

Butler Bob

Patrick Holloway

Butler Bob, as he was known to all except his mother, was a queer fish. From the way he shuffled up and down Cotter's Rd, to the way he mumbled indistinguishable words under his bad breath. But he was a nice enough guy. Wouldn't harm a fly, people would say, or, not a bad bone in his body has Butler Bob. And if his name was ever mentioned an image would be conjured up of him shuffling with his hands in his pockets, or the white of Guinness on an unshaved upper lip, or even the odd image of him smoking a rolled-up cigarette. Funny how nobody remembered him as a child. Butler Bob, it seemed, came into existence at around forty.

He had a clan of brothers and sisters, as was the fashion way back when. Younger and older, dead and alive, and he was always somewhere in the middle. In the background. A corner of his head here or his long, bony fingers on a sibling's shoulder. His face, even in family albums, is a phantom. Pauletta, the youngest of the sisters has only one memory of him as a child and that is this:

The older brothers and Butler Bob were all going boxing with their father. This had become a new hobby forced upon them all because Butler Bob's father seemed to think Butler Bob could be a little soft in the head, a little weak in the knees; he feared he'd been sprinkled with fairy dust, so he said to his wife, he said: Miriam, I'm taking the boys boxing, nothing a good box can't beat out of a boy. And who was Miriam to argue. Who was Miriam at all. So, this one day, young Pauletta was asked to go along and so off she went. And she remembers being stuck in between the boys in the back of their father's van with the smell of sawdust and sweat, and she remembers looking at Butler Bob's knobbly knees. And coming up to the boxing hall she remembers the sounds of bags being punched and the squeaking of trainers on rubber, and the clattering of metal lockers. Inside she sat on a hard wooden bench and the walls were made of concrete and the paint was all fading. And it was dark, dim, dank, and from the corner of the hall there was a light coming from a room and she looked over and saw Butler Bob stepping out as if onto a stage, his knobbly knees shaking and big boxing gloves stemming from his twig like arms and the space between him and the boxing ring seemed infinite. And as he walked out and crossed the hall, Pauletta saw the silhouette of a naked man cross the room. And that is the only memory she has of Butler Bob as a boy.

The truth was Butler Bob had a lot to offer the world when he was locked up in the privacy of his loneliness. If truth be told he thought himself somewhat special. Who else can drink ten pints of Guinness and still walk in a straight line, he'd think to himself, or who else can name all the counties in Ireland in alphabetical order, who indeed except Butler Bob. Antrim, Armagh, Carlow, Cavan, he'd whisper to himself. Backwards too, he could do it. Wicklow, Wexford, Westmeath, Waterford. And what about being able to bend his right thumb backwards as if confusing the space around his thumb, or his whistling rendition of *Today*, by John Denver! He did think of himself as somewhat special but then he'd walk out into the big bluey green world and get asked for the time and have trouble deciphering the big hand from the small hand. Stumbling over words with spittle at his lips, the person - Mary Maguire, in the case a few weeks back - who had asked the question would politely nod and go about their day, maybe later to tell a friend, while sipping Malbec from the Mendoza region, of a strange man they met on the street.

They often say you can tell a lot about somebody from their possessions. Mary Maguire had many possessions. Had a bed-side locker full of rings and necklaces bought from cities in countries she had visited and couldn't remember the name of. She had expensive art hanging on her walls; art by fairly-famous artists, and she would not talk about the art but talk about the artist. She had three drawers full of shoes, some still unworn. Yes, they say you can tell a lot about somebody from their possessions. Pauletta picked her possessions like princesses choose princes. She would often spend minutes picking up a wooden-carved robin-red-breast she had bought years earlier and hold it in her hands and think back on the day, the time; she often remembered exactly the price she had bought it for, down to the very cent. Her house looked like something from a magazine- in the very best way. Pauletta, it could be said, from her possessions, was a classy lady.

Butler Bob wasn't a man for possessions. Even if he had the money for them, he wouldn't put much thought into them at all. For all they did was take up space and he couldn't understand for the life of him why space needed to be taken up. Space, to him, was a rather wonderful thing. Space between his hand and the pint; space between the stool and the bar, and between him and the barman. The space that twisted and turned its way up Cotter's Rd, and on again to the cliffs that look out on Cork harbour and then all that space weighing the sea down. And what about the space beyond the horizon, he thought, what about all that space. Why you would want to fill that space up was beyond Butler Bob.

If we're on the same page about possessions and what they say about a person, than we could assume Butler Bob was a minimalist.

His sitting room had two chairs - one with a cushion and one without - a small desk used as a dining-table that also had a drawer, and in that drawer was a lighter, a box of matches, a black and white photo, and a gold chain left to him by his father. The kitchen was of a similar fashion. A couple of plates, knives and forks taken from random bars in the village, pint glasses taken from one specific pub in the village, some corn flakes, milk, and so on.

His mattress lay on the wooden floorboards and he had a little lamp on the right side of the mattress. The mattress had a sheet, a thick, hand-knitted blanket, and two pillows - one with a pillow-case and one without. There was a book next to the mattress. The book was called *Breakfast of Champions* and written by a man that Butler Bob thought of as a kind of God.

So there we have it. Butler Bob and his possessions didn't add up to all that much. If Butler Bob had thought about his lack of possessions he might have known that there were groups forming all around the world; groups of minimalists trying to make a statement about something or other. If Butler Bob had known about these groups he might well have joined one only to be disappointed to find that it was full of people who once had many, many possessions and went running round the house in fits and spurts of madness, asking themselves, *do I really need this?* Butler Bob would have found it all a little bit forced and he'd have gotten lost in the monologue-like conversations they'd conduct in order to make themselves feel different. He wouldn't understand the eight syllable words they used incorrectly, or the way they nodded their heads with such ferocity. He'd have thought that they themselves were taker-uppers of space.

The reason the story of Butler Bob is on the tongues of all the local cats at the moment is because Butler Bob hasn't been seen in around 26 days. His last appearance, according to Johnny the barman, was on the Friday night (28 days ago) when he ordered a pint of Guinness only to sip at the warming beer for over an hour and leave without ever paying Johnny the barman. Philip, the local manager of the grocery shop, claims to have sold Butler Bob a large head of cabbage on the Saturday. (27 days ago) There are many more 'witnesses' of Butler Bob, some say the saw him catch the 222 bus into the city; others say they saw him hitchhiking by Glenwood's cross. Mary Maguire claims to have asked Butler Bob the time on the Sunday (26 days ago) and told her friends that he seemed to be in an awful state altogether. *I had never spoken to him myself,* she had said, *but he did seem like an awful queer fish.* To that her friends nodded and sighed and swirled their wine around in their glasses. One lit a cigarette and told them that she'd once kissed him back in school. She had been a friend of Pauletta at the time and had been over in her house and while Pauletta was getting ready she was left with Butler Bob sitting on the sofa. *He put his hand on my knee,* she told her friends, all of them leaning forward. *And then I turned to him and he kissed me hard on the mouth and then ran out of the room. I heard a door slam upstairs and it sounded like he was crying.* The women bit their lips and sipped their wine and thought of what a strange specimen Butler Bob must have been.

Pauletta had seen him on the Wednesday (30 days ago) when she had bumped into him walking up the Lower Rd. She had just visited a friend and had a glass or two or three of wine and decided to walk home. Something she never did. She was of that era that didn't need to abide by the new drink-driving laws. Sure after all, it was only up the road. But on this Wednesday, 30 days ago, she decided to leave the car and walk home. Something must have been on her mind, something a bit of fresh air might help. She hadn't walked 100 yards and had bumped into Butler Bob. His curly hair a mess, standing on edge and pointing out in all directions; his cheeks reddened by drink, by time, by space. There were days she'd be walking past a mirror in the morning, before make up had been applied, or hair had been combed, and she'd get a flash of Butler Bob looking back at her. Looking at him then, on the Lower Rd, she thought of his face like a shadow of a great monument. She'd have moments when she'd think thoughts like that, and think to herself, if only I could write. But that's what he looked like to her, then, with the sun high in the sky, he looked like a shadow a monument would leave fall upon the ground.

Where are you off to, asks Pauletta, the only one with a memory of Butler Bob as a boy.

Out strolling, he answered, without looking at her. He could have been talking to anyone, in fact, he was. He was such a flustered state that he didn't realise it was his youngest sister he was talking to for he kept his eyes on his feet and the space between the left and the right.

He hurried past her without another word. Pauletta found it strange, but then again she thought a lot about Butler Bob strange. And it was in that moment that she remembered Butler Bob at the boxing hall, and how the light came from the room and poor old Butler Bob seemed to be walking onto a stage, and the silhouette of a naked man fading from sight; fading into empty space.

This was the last time Butler Bob was seen. Johnny the barman had served him that pint of Guinness a week earlier, and Philip the manager was an awful gossip who'd say he sold a head of cabbage to the devil if he thought it would lengthen a conversation. And Mary Maguire had mixed up Sunday with Tuesday, for they are the two days a week she plays tennis.

Of course Butler Bob would be found. And of course the ending is not a happy one. For everything is found, anything that takes up space will be found; space itself, as Butler Bob found out, is inedible, indestructible, uncapturable, and the more you take of it the more you lose your way. The only way to not occupy space, Butler Bob deduced, was to not occupy space at all.

The God Who Was Himself Whispered In Her Ear

Carole Burns

If she could lose herself in the story, Serena thought, she could get over their fraught morning. The audience in the airy, white lobby of the Wales Millennium Centre began to settle down as the storyteller walked onto the stage, crossed it once or twice, then stood, tall and still, his long blond hair in a 1970s ponytail, his face bright red as if he'd "caught the sun" (one of her favorite new phrases). This is so British! she thought. In an alternative kind of way, not in a way she could have ever imagined in the States. Her plan of steeping herself in Britishness to soothe the homesickness she always felt when she and Rich argued was beginning to work.

The audience fell silent – even the customers in the cafés, the people streaming past on their way to other events, seemed to quiet into a hush as the storyteller began.

"One day — " his chin jutting out as he spoke – "a fool found an ancient coin on the ground near a wishing well. Roman? the fool wondered, intrigued for a moment."

Rich shifted next to her as if already bored. "... no great find in this ancient land." Unless he was still angry? *Stop it!*

She shut her eyes as she sometimes did when she was read to, trying to take in the story, the storyteller's voice, trying again to block out the sense of loneliness that had come over her that morning like nausea as she waited for Rich to return from the distant planet of his ex-wife, every other person she loved an ocean away. *Listen!* she whispered to herself.

"… no point selling the coin on eBay; he would use it to make a wish. But what should he wish for? He might have been a fool but he knew people less foolish than he had blown their wishes on silly, selfish, superficial desires – for money (which never brought happiness) or beautiful women (who didn't love them). And when he finally thought of his – to be a lucky man – he tossed the coin toward the wishing well. It arced into the air, and as it was falling as neatly as a rugby ball kicked by a Wales No. 10, a magpie flew from nowhere, caught the coin in midair, and vanished again. Our friend didn't even have time to salute the lone bird and cancel out the destiny of sorrow that the single magpie had just delivered to him."

" 'Enough of this nonsense,' the fool said to himself, and to anyone else who would listen. 'Wishing wells and magpies, my foot. I'm going to find God and find out why I'm so unlucky.' And so he left, walking over hill, down into the dale, across the M4, and into the forest…"

The small audience laughed. Serena was pleased that she, too, had gotten the British jokes – even the rugby reference, though there was no way anyone could live with Richie and not learn to love sports a little (well, except for you-know-who). She caressed his leg, stole a quick look to see how he was, her rather Anglicised but still fellow American. Pubs, Welsh rugby, Indian food were what he liked about the U.K. Cathedrals, male voice choirs, storytellers were not. He smiled back vaguely.

Good enough, she thought. And as she listened, rapt, eyes open now, the storyteller began to take the shape of the characters in his fable: optimistic, like the fool, as he stepped lightly, springily, from one end of the stage to the other; his deep, reedy voice threatening, like the hungry wolf in the forest as he asked the fool to seek God's advice on where he might find more food. Upright and thin, the storyteller became the straggly tree that asked the man to find out why it could drink no water despite being planted by a clear blue lake. With his thick, yellow locks, the man turned into the beautiful woman in the pretty red house and a green, green garden, who asked the fool to find out from God why she was still so unhappy. Finally, the storyteller became the God whom the fool, once he finally tracked him down, found juggling apples in a tree, telling the man, as the apples went round and round, round and round, mesmerizing the audience with the hint of eternity, that luck was always there for the finding: go look for it.

"So the fool took God's advice," the storyteller said, "and turned around to set off for home. On his way, he passed the beautiful woman once again, who wanted to know how he had fared. 'Well,' the fool told her happily, 'God said that I simply need to go find my luck.' 'And did you ask him about me?' She spoke tentatively, not knowing if she wanted to hear what this God had to say. 'Oh yes,' the fool said, 'you are unhappy because you have no one to share your life with; beautiful things are always better shared.' 'Well, man,' she said, reaching her pale arm out to him lightly, 'would you stay with me and share my house, my garden, my life?' The fool answered immediately. 'Oh no, I can't. I must go find my luck!' And off he went."

Serena stole a look at Rich. Was he listening? He clasped her hand and rolled his eyes at her; he was enjoying it despite himself.

"And when the man reached the tree and related what God had said, the tree, too, asked about his case. 'Oh yes,' the man told him, 'God said that there is a treasure buried in the roots of your tree. You must find someone to dig up the treasure, and then your roots will be free to soak up water again.' 'Oh, man,' said the tree, 'would you be kind enough to dig up that treasure for me?' The fool responded immediately. 'Oh, no, I don't have time, I must go find my luck!' And off he went, through the forest, where he again met the wolf, and he repeated his story. 'And what,' the wolf growled, 'did God say about me.' 'Ah, yes,' the man said. 'He said you must eat the first fool you see.' And so — " the storyteller stood motionless, for a moment, then his voice rang out like a laugh " — the wolf did."

As the audience clapped, Serena found herself close to tears. Was this her fate, too — would Richie never see? Their argument, leading a train of other, similar arguments, came rushing back. Didn't he know he had to appreciate what life had thrown his way? But this was an old story for her and Rich, too. She turned away so he wouldn't detect her tears.

Rich watched with part affection, part annoyance, as Serena went up to talk to the storyteller. He liked her American habit of having to meet everybody, talk to everybody, tell everybody how good they were. He still, found it refreshing, as if his twenty years in the U.K. had made him one of them; it wasn't something Beth would have ever done. Would ever do, he corrected himself. She wasn't dead. Sometimes, though, he wished Serena could make a quicker exit.

The Millennium Centre was crowded on this Saturday afternoon in April; people rushed to the Bay on these rare sunny days, families mostly, or couples on their own, streaming through the arts centre as if was part of a tour. He liked the inside of the building better than the hulking outside (it looks like Darth Vader, Serena always said): the way the stairs angled up two stories past the balconies, how the words cut into the steel façade at the front became, from within, just geometric patterns like the stairs and the balconies. It couldn't have been an easy place to perform – perhaps the storyteller's presence of mind was as impressive as his story. The space echoed like a playground: the screeching children, the chattering parents, the chairs like park benches, the cafés the ice cream truck, the banisters the slides. He felt a pang: how he missed his daughters, his family, the Saturday afternoons when he and the girls and maybe Beth, if she were feeling well, would have ended up here, too.

Serena was still standing happily at the back of the queue of people waiting to speak to the storyteller; she had let a few people go ahead of her, so she wouldn't feel rushed. Rich wished suddenly he had gone up with her, was holding her hand; for as she reached the man and leaned forward to speak, her flaming red hair flashing over her shoulder, the storyteller stood taller and looked around him with a ridiculous, twinkly smile as if wondering if anyone else was noticing his surprising stroke of luck. Amid the couples walking past hand in hand, children skipping ahead of their parents, Serena and the storyteller stood in their own bubble, their bodies dipping toward and away from one another, exchanging business cards, cash and a CD.

Then Serena was standing in front of Rich as if she had been spirited there from the future. He kissed her quickly, hoping the other man would see; she was all atwitter. "He lives in Canton!" she said excitedly. "I've invited him to dinner!"

They left the Centre to take the walk they had planned, passing the petite black-roofed Norwegian Church ("it's so *cute*," Serena said again) then reaching the barrage that stretched over the Bay to Penarth, where they'd stop for lunch. This walk was the main reason he'd agreed to hear the storyteller, though it would have seemed churlish not to after their argument, after she'd said how homesick she'd felt. Beth had asked him to come to the house to watch the girls for just half an hour, Serena telling him, quietly, She. Can. Bring Them. Here. Crying when he'd said he'd be right back, it made more sense to go there. And it had. Serena seemed better now, the storyteller, the walk over the Bay, doing its trick. "Maybe we could take the girls to see him," she said, her head bopping up and down beside him as she walked with her little bounce, "he says he does children's events, do you think they'd like this walk, though it's too long, maybe we could take the ferry over and walk from the Penarth side, they'd love that!" A little girl ran by with her nose dripping in the chill air, but with Serena buoyant next to him, his thought – he'd wipe his own girls' runny noses with his bare hand – had lost its sting.

This was how he needed her to be – his beacon through all this darkness. "Shine bright," he wanted to tell her. "Keep shining bright." Instead he pulled her to the side of the bridge and kissed her. "You're gorgeous – do you know that?" She kissed him back through her smile, her eyes wet from cold or tears or maybe both, her breast pushed against his chest. He adored her. Her cold soft cheek against his, her girlish excitement about the storyteller, even her emphatic tears this morning as he left the house because he couldn't wait to get back to her; he was bound to help Beth first but he couldn't wait to escape to Serena. "What the hell are we doing on a bridge?" he grumbled into her ear. So they went home, to bed, Serena pointing out in the car, "God *did* say to find our own luck," at home pulling off his jeans, "we are lucky, lucky, lucky" kissing his stomach, wrapping her legs around his waist, "lucky, lucky," until she couldn't speak for moaning.

Months later, Serena settled into a couch in the storyteller's house but did not look at him as he talked and talked, as her new friend tended to do, the new friend whom she had somewhat purposefully chosen to make plans with for the evening – the evening Rich was having dinner with his daughters at his ex-wife's house without her. Serena would never be invited to celebrate the girls' graduating from nursery school, or to celebrate anything else. Ever. Rich went anyway. Distraction, she needed distraction, she couldn't possibly sit home and stew over Rich's cozy family dinner, and she knew the storyteller, raconteur that he was over coffee, at her and Rich's house, and now at his own home, would distract her. He had the knack of seeming as if he was paying attention just to her, or whoever else he was talking to – though Rich thought it was just Serena. He couldn't take his eyes off her. So Rich said. He didn't much approve of her friendship with the storyteller, but tonight he couldn't exactly complain.

Now, at the storyteller's house, she was stewing nonetheless. Did children really graduate from nursery school? It sounded like a lovey-dovey aren't-our-children-wonderful fabrication concocted by Beth to pull Rich into her web. It sounded American, even, as if she'd begun using tools from her enemy's arsenal. *We can celebrate with the girls ourselves!* Serena had said, *And we will!* Rich had said. But the real celebration, the one that counted, Serena knew, was tonight; theirs would be a weak afterthought. Enough, enough. She remembered the storyteller used to be a clown. Maybe he could perform some slapstick for her: pretend to bump his head on the door, trip over the step into the kitchen. He had performed for twenty years with his wife, he'd told her a few weeks ago, until she moved out. He didn't seem haunted by her, though hints of his past, his own sadness, snuck out now and then – in some ways it was why she liked him.

She dared to look at him – she'd been avoiding his gaze all evening – and his blue eyes, startling in color, but also startling in expression, as if they'd just seen something absolutely amazing, were watching her as if waiting. He stood up quickly and stepped toward her then away then went over and picked up an apple from the cluttered coffee table as if he might juggle just one then sat down again. Books, a small flash light, a tea cup, a pair of castanets, were strewn across the table like an unruly still life; she wondered if he gathered them for inspiration.

"Your stories were great the other night," she said. "I wish the girls could have come." Beth had switched nights on Rich at the last minute (more bullshit). She tried to mention Rich and the girls when she could with the storyteller, when naturally she might. It seemed necessary. "Rich didn't have the girls after all."

"That's a shame. Though another venue would be better for them."

She nodded. He had told the story again of the unlucky fool, but this time she was listening alone in a small café, Rich staying home to watch a football match instead. "You didn't juggle," she said.

He laughed. "Forgot the balls. I added the juggling right before I told it at the Millennium Centre. I don't know if you noticed but a few people laughed at that part of the story — friends. Because I used to end my act that way, juggling. So I had made myself God."

"The story makes me tearful," she admitted.

"Oh, why?" He asked it casually, off-hand, as if this were still a light conversation.

Here was territory she hadn't entered with the storyteller; confessing her problems with Richie seemed another kind of invitation which she didn't want to extend. Yet did. "Well, you know. It's people not seeing what's in front of them. The treasures in front of them."

"Ah," he said. "Carpe Diem." The storyteller looked strangely at her, then down at the apple in his hand.

"What is it?" she asked. "I've made you sad again." Was he thinking of his ex-wife? Serena always worried that she dragged his grief out of him as if he were Rich; out, out, damn spot, out. She didn't want to make the storyteller sad just because she was – but what was it then? "I can't read your face."

He shook his head. "I don't know why you'd say that."

And she thought for a moment that he didn't agree with her interpretation of his tale – isn't it obvious? she almost said – then realised he didn't understand what she'd said right then, about the sadness in his face.

Rich left his old house – his ex-wife's house – and headed home. Not his new home – he imagined telling Serena – just home. He wanted her to know it was how he thought of it in his head. He would tell her that, he thought, unlocking his door, calling out into the seemingly empty house. "Serena?

Sweetie?" He would tell her that was what he thought on his way back from Beth's, give her that small gift in exchange, as recompense, for what he suddenly could see might have been a difficult night. "Serena?" But she wasn't home. The house seemed especially vacant, though it always did after leaving the girls. He packed away all the girls' toys to send back to Beth, although Serena didn't understand why some toys couldn't live here. His insistence that it was neater always seemed foolish after leaving the haphazard mess of girly objects in Beth's house.

She must still be with the storyteller. He'd been dying to come home to her; feel her body; remind himself why he had done all this. He wondered if he should worry.

Then the phone rang out. His heart lifted and he went over to pick it up. "Hi Sweetie," he answered to deep silence.

"Uh, Beth, actually," his ex-wife said.

She'd called because she had forgotten to discuss arrangements for the weekend, though really the plans were the same as always. He'd pick the girls up around six, giving Beth an hour to spend with them after work; he wasn't sure what variation she needed to discuss. *She does this on purpose,* he could hear Serena say, *so she can call you again, here.* But it wasn't true, he knew Beth, she was just forgetful, he wouldn't admit even the slightest possibility of manipulation on her part, even if Serena wasn't the only friend who'd called Beth manipulative, even if for half a second after each extra phone call he suspected Serena might be right, but they were wrong, they didn't know her.

He and Beth confirmed their weekend plans and she thanked him for coming over for dinner. "The girls loved it," she said and he flushed with pride. *This is why*, he would tell Serena, *This is why*.

"So that's what you call her then?" Beth said. "Sweetie?"

Rich stood still. What was he supposed to say? Yes?

"I mean, I'm so glad you came over, it was so good for the girls, but this is so—" she began to break down, the tears coming fast now, "so hard for me. I can't believe how hard it still is, I still don't understand, why, why did you do this, how could you do this *to them*, why…"

"Beth, please," he said. He let her cry at him for twenty, forty, he'd lost track, maybe sixty minutes. *Hang up,* he heard Serena say. Thank God she wasn't here.

"Can I try your piano?" Serena asked the storyteller.

So many books and CDs and magazines and even a bright orange wig perhaps from his clowning days, or his ex-wife's, were piled on top of the keyboard cover that Serena wondered about the symbolism of these obstacles – he had clearly not been the piano player in the house. She was about to tell him not to bother when he began moving the items away.

"I'd be honored," he said, and he whisked them onto the coffee table, the window sill.

"Are you going to juggle all this?"

He obligingly tossed one light book in the air and looked pleased to catch it on his head. She laughed so he threw another backward, bouncing it off his heel. And then the piano was clear. She lifted the lid to reveal the ivory keys. "Now you're entertaining me," he said.

"Oh, I'm not very good," but she tinkled a few notes while she leafed through his music. Not too out of tune; maybe he did play. "Will you juggle to Ragtime?"

He shook his head. "Play something serious," and he leaned against the windowsill.

She looked back at him and stood to shuffle through his partner's Chopin, Mozart, Beethoven, then she put it all away and sat down again. "This is my homesickness singing," and she played Shenandoah. "Oh Shenandoah, I long to see you," half singing, half humming the words, "mmm, hmm, mmm, you rolling river," thinking of home, of Richie, of the blackness in his eyes when he missed his girls, of the emptiness in her when he wasn't there, "hmm-hmm-hmm, I'm bound away," her voice low, and the storyteller hummed a harmony above her, their voices mingling. He stepped closer and stood beside her near the bench, his hand close to her shoulder. The god in his story whispered in her ear: *Carpe Diem*.

She stopped, her head down.

"Serena."

She felt him breathing next to her, waiting. The sound of the silent piano filled the room. He could touch her now, he could kiss her. Would that help?

"You know your story?" she asked. "About the unlucky man?"

"Yes?"

"I always think it's Richie being the fool, not appreciating his life. Not appreciating me." She looked up, tears wet on her face. "What if I'm the fool?"

"Ah," he said, and stepped away. She turned back to the piano and clinked on a few keys. She wondered what he would do now, from the distance she hadn't meant to create.

"Play it again," he said. "I'll juggle to this."

And he stepped across the room gathering the apple, a ceramic pear that he'd said his sister-in-law had made, an orange. "This song's too slow!" Serena protested but she heard her own voice, lighter, laughing, and the notes from the piano flew off her fingers fast and jolly. He turned to stand before her juggling the three objects, apple, orange and pear going round and round, round and round.

'til human voices wake us
Jo Mazelis

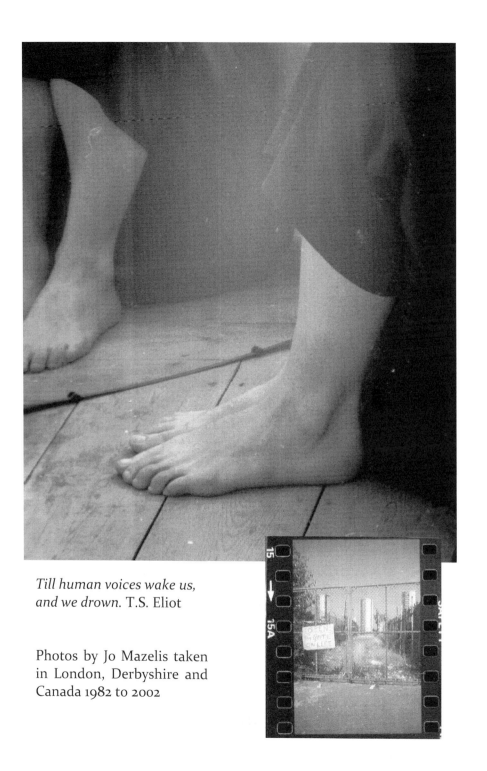

Till human voices wake us,
and we drown. T.S. Eliot

Photos by Jo Mazelis taken
in London, Derbyshire and
Canada 1982 to 2002

Three Poems
Kathy Miles

WALKING IN BRONANT

Softly on these late roads sun speckles
through like dapples on a Welsh mare.
A badger moon, striped with cloud, noses
autumn into the darkening sky
and a wind sharpened by September mist
shakes handfuls of sparrows from the oak.

Hazel, its branches looped from the ground
like a Menorah, lit by pale husks.
Brooches of clover embedded in stone,
ivy snaking rusty iron gates. Love-in-vain
twists through the ruins, unfurling
each morning, the flag of an old empire.

The dry remains of poplar lean against
the walls of a once-lush garden.
Here the chaffinch endlessly mourns,
and lacewings strum a delicate arc

above the blurred outlines of flowerbeds,
hover over a trace of silted river.

A buzzard's thin sostenuto layers along
the dust: crickets clack in yellowed grass.
The air is full of the must of pollen,
musky roses trapped in a fragrant past.
Our words shimmer like dragonflies
on the cusp of evening light.

Your blue dress blown by the breeze
so your body is held in a muffle of fabric.
And I remember how your heart howled
like a squall that last November.
Pulling up your roots, felling you,
the loss spiralling as blown acorns,
the scud of the owl's shrill cry.

INHERITING ALICE

Her name shimmers on my tongue, like a taste
I can't identify. Eighty five years gone,
and the pain of missing her shafts through my DNA.
One photograph, faded now. Framed by trees
and bracken, two children squinting at the sun.
Her hands are still. But I know how raw
and chapped the palms were, skin rough
from washing clothes on winter days.

I take the weight of her name into my mouth,
breathe in the word of her, all the pages
she might have been, reach down and drag her
up through the years, clasp her hand,
her dark eyes ghosting my own.

If I gave back the features I have borrowed,
my mother would get the hair that never curls,
my father, this long and melancholy face.
But to you, Alice, I'd return
that shy glance at the camera's lens,
the quirky purse of lips, my awkward smile.

The quiet bleach of things. Centuries laid out
like sheets at night, a slow dissolve

in moonlight. The only record in the owl's
wingbeat as he soars over churchyards,
the inscription on each headstone
etched into his soul.

And this is where I find you, Alice,
asleep beneath harebell and sorrel,
overgrown, forgotten,
except for that space in the grail of my head
where you are still waiting.

SLATE

In winter, this road would be a harsh drive.
The valley quickened with frost,
the culverts frozen. Fields fly past

like blown birds, childhood coming
closer with each mile, last rosebay
hanging to the margins.

A slow graze of sheep. The ewes
loose and sullen, slumped beside verges,
cropping the flint grass, wandering

beyond known boundaries, their own lineage.
And above, wet quires of slate, rising
in steep cliffs, a slew of stone slipping

to the track. Blue-grey, glas,
the colour of gull or merlin.

At this final stage the year is weary.

Only a flare of gorse on the bleak slopes,
the smell of mountains heathered into rain.
At the end of the journey you greet us.

Frailer now, wary as a lamb, cast
in the caul of our friendship.
Our mutual past bleating its shared memory,

like a mother calling in its young,
crying to the wind, the lost newborn.
Fracturing my heart.

Some Justice
Armel Dagorn

When I start the car and leave the estate for my night's round, the headlights sweep across the bare concrete of unfinished houses. They briefly light up the faces of squatters wrapped up in rags, and sometimes reach the inside of the stillborn buildings, where more destitutes huddle around plywood fires. I draw looks, I know. First, of course, because a Ferrari is not something you see every day. Or maybe they look at me because they know me, because they've seen me around, have heard of me. I know there are rumours. And if they don't know me, and the Ferrari isn't enough to tickle their curiosity, the mask surely does the trick.

I sewed it myself, by hand, a strip ripped from my son's Slipknot t-shirt and fashioned into a Zorro-like mask. At first I thought the very idea of a mask ridiculous, but I need to protect myself. I find the impression it leaves on thieves gives me a much needed advantage. My first, uninspired choice had been a regular balaclava, but on my inaugural patrol wearing it, I had found myself in a house facing two hoodlums who stopped in their tracks when they saw me, wondering who I was. They'd felt perhaps a kinship between us despite my suit and tie, as if I was a freelancer hoping to get on the team. The strange uncertainty of that instant had sapped my morale, and I'd wrestled with them with less than my usual strength. They ended up getting away, and I had to flee in their tracks when the police arrived and saw me, balaclavaed, coming out of the house.

In the car, heading out for the night, I put on music. Woody Guthrie first: *Vigilante man*. I'd listened to it a few times, humming along, my mind focused on the dark streets, before I realised the vigilante of the song was a villain, a strike-breaking boogeyman. I still listen to it every night, singing the chorus softly. It's just that I like the word: vigilante. A vigilant man, someone who's able to look ahead and see trouble before it comes. From a dictionary I leafed through in a house I saved: "alertly watchful". The lyrics have disappointed me, but the melancholy of the song suits my new home, the dreary grey buildings where ghosts live. It suits the night and its menace, and it suits me.

Recently I've taken to starting the night by driving by our old house. I know I shouldn't, that it won't change a thing and doesn't do me any good, except maybe by reminding me what I'm out there to protect, the life which needs to be saved. I stand there in the front yard, looking at the house, at the lit windows, glimpses into the happy life of another family. I stand and think about Rebecca and Julian. The carefree days we spent there. I try to put myself in her shoes, but it's hard. Despite all I lost, the bankruptcy, I feel like our family could have survived. In my book, as long as we were together, even if we had to live in one of these windowless house shells, it would have been OK. I try not to be bitter.

Tonight, as I am losing myself in my own gloom on my former lawn, I hear the sound of clinking metal and when I look down the road I see a man stooping over the driver's door of Colm McKenna's Mercedes. I walk up to him, and when I'm close enough, I shout "You!" pointing at him with my baseball bat. He takes the slim jim out of the door, and for a second he brandishes it menacingly, like a sword. I know that kid. He's sixteen, at most, a scrawny teenager not unlike my son. He lives in one of the first houses of the abandoned estate, with other young ones. They're often outside when I leave at night, drinking cider from two-litre bottles, warming up around an oil drum fire.

He runs off. There is no point giving pursuit: I have bigger fish to fry. I take out my notebook, and scribble down the first intervention of the night.

11.26 – 16 Maple Dr, Teen brk in Mercedes S600, pl. 11-D-16425 (belong. C. McKenna) R.Away, no arrest.

As I put the notebook back in my breast pocket, I hear a familiar voice behind me.

"Isaac?" It's Brian, whose hedge trimmer I used to borrow. His voice is soft, unsure. He stands there in his dressing gown, a few steps away from me, his hand half raised as if approaching a wild animal.

I start walking towards my car. "Isaac, hey, wait." He follows me. "Why don't you come in for a bit? Have a cup of tea?" I get in the Ferrari. Muffled by the door, I hear him again before I turn the key in the ignition. "We should talk, Isaac..."

Of course it's a bad idea for me to go back to the house, to stand there on the lawn like a sentimental old fool. I don't belong here anymore. The right to be among these grand houses is something I lost along with my money. On my first rounds, my first successfully thwarted burglaries, I used to hang around the houses I'd protected, waiting for their owners to come home from their night out in town, at the opera, at the restaurant, and I would step in as they walked up to their front door, tell them about the danger avoided, their valuables saved. They recoiled from me, because of the mask maybe, but mostly because I am marked. They could tell I wasn't like them anymore. Maybe more than the sight of a strange man with a mask appearing on their front yard at night, wanting to talk to them, it was my aura that made them withdraw. Couples hugged each other, inching towards the door as I told them how I had defeated the men threatening their possessions. Maybe they could tell I slept in my car, could smell the blend of leather from the seats, of the take-away wrappers which littered the Ferrari's floor in these early, depressed days, and of Rebecca's jumper. I still use it as a pillow, even though any hint of her perfume has long been replaced by my own musk. When I left I knew they'd call the police, giving them my description rather than my report on the burglars. I've learnt to deal differently with my interventions. When I catch thieves I tie them up and leave the door open, then wait for the police hidden in a bush, in somebody's garden. Otherwise I just leave a note.

I don't belong anymore in the quiet suburbs I've lived in all my life. I only patrol them at night now, when they're not too shockingly different from the empty estate where I park my car-home during the day. I have tried to drive through them in daylight, but found it unbearable. The colourful façades, the flowers, cars, the children playing and laughing: I can't live among all that anymore, my place is in its negative, in the streets of unfinished houses.

I drive around, trying to get Brian and my early mistakes out of my mind. I am a few hours into my round, and apart from the car-stealing attempt nothing else has turned up. This is the time when opportunistic robberies end, these quick, haphazard jobs during house owners' nights out. Soon the more professional thieves move in, targeting houses they know will be empty for the night. Usually I need a little pick-me-up at that stage, and I drive down to the 24-hour McDonald's for coffee. I pull a baseball cap down low on my face to hide the mask as the girl hands me the cup through the window, and when I drive away I take Woody Guthrie out of the machine and feed it something upbeat. Sometimes disco, sometimes good old rock and roll.

Tonight it's Marvin Gaye. "What's going on," he sings, and I sing along, and I'm still singing under my breath as I park the car in a side street and get out. I've seen a van parked in front of an unlit house, a man sitting alone at the wheel, his head rocking to a boom-boom which reaches me dulled. I sneak up through the neighbours' gardens, running in a half-crouch, until I'm in a shrub a few steps away from the house. In an instant I'm against the wall, then slowly slide to the window, and in the gap between the half-closed curtains I see a living-room, and two dark figures running their torches over the furniture. A three-man job. Classic. I'm used to these, to quickly overpowering one, then two men, then the third, usually the moron of the group waiting in the get-away car, too dumb to not yield to boredom, to take the watchman's job seriously. I am not a very strong man, but I am now quite experienced in the kicking of robbers' asses. I've grown fit in the past few months. I am leaner, more streamlined without the pouch which used to announce me everywhere I went. I spend a long time, every day, jogging, lifting bricks and breeze blocks, trying to make myself into a perfect crime-fighting machine. But it's mostly the diet, really. Gone are the rich, feasty meals of my family days. Now I live on what I glean, here and there, in the houses I save. Like a small tax on justice. I often wonder if in the aftermath of a burglary families realise that an apple is missing, or a couple of slices of bread and a bit of cheese. Or the pennies I collect for my midnight coffee.

I walk to the back of the house. The door is open, its glass pane shattered. I enter the kitchen with my ears pricked up like a bat's, tuned to the sounds of the dark house. From there I go into the corridor, follow the hushed voices and footsteps to the living-room. They're not that discreet, and just as I stand by the doorway, I hear one of the two men burst out laughing. He has a very youthful voice, almost childish. I peek in and see them both standing their backs to me, appraising the huge flat-screen TV which fills a corner of the room. I tiptoe towards them, raising my bat, ready to smash it down on the closest man's knee. I hear the slightest tread on the carpet behind me, then feel an unbearable pain explode in my head for a split second, before losing consciousness.

The black-out doesn't last, and I wake up on the floor of the living-room, the pain in my head quickly drowning out under the pain all over my body, as feet and batons rain onto me. I curl up in a ball but the blows keep coming, from every direction. There's loads of them, young ones, all in their teens probably.

"Hey, hey!" I hear then, over the abuse they shout at me between kicks. "It's OK, leave him." I see a face parting the wall of my tormentors. It's the young fellow I stopped earlier. How did he go from a wannabe car thief to a burglar in one night? I realise then these kids are not what I'm used to,

166

they're not like the reliable, professional thieves I usually deal with at that time of night.

I feel like I'm on the brink of something, unconsciousness probably, or worse. I know I should be scared, that it is what the situation calls for, but I'm quite at peace, lulled by the youths' voices. A weird thought comes to me: I'm happy for a second Julian doesn't want to see me anymore, or tomorrow, if it comes, I would have had to lie again, to make up some job interview out of town to explain why I couldn't make the monthly week-end visit. How many times had that happened, how many times had robbers covered my face in bruises?

I feel a sharp pain in the ribs.

"Leave him be," the boy says.

"He's that old guy who lives in the estate."

"That mental fuck? They say he's a mad car. Like, a Jaguar or shit." The voice comes from out back, and I wonder how many of them there are. They're a new breed of criminals, these boys, born into it, moving in packs. I feel hands all over me, burrowing into my pockets for my keys.

"Who does he work for?" I feel drowsy, but I force my eyelids to stay open.

"Don't know, but can't be paying that much. I've heard he goes through bins for food."

"Crazy cunt." I hear a throat clearing, feel a ball of spit hit my cheek.

"Come on lads, let's go," says the car thief, and I catch him giving me a quick look before walking away. There's pity in his eyes. They leave, but it seems to take forever before they're all gone, and some of them give me a farewell kick. So many of them do, when I'm finally alone and replay their exit in my head I find it impossible to count the kicks.

I lay there, unable to move. Whenever I try, an incredibly sharp pain bursts in my back. There is something very wrong there. Soon I hear a siren approaching, growing from a faint whine into a loud bark just outside the house. They will burst in, guns in hand, push me face down and handcuff me, heedless of my broken body. They will take off my mask then. Take me away.

What We Burned in the Fire
Dan Coxon

Rory was the one who found it. He'd been scouting ahead, whacking the heads off the long grass with a stick. I was lagging behind, the sweat sticking my t-shirt to my body like a second skin. I saw him stop, then he called out, not bothering to turn his head.

"Hey! Come look at this!"

I saw the gnarly mass before I reached his shoulder, its peak as high as the yellowing grass. I had no idea what it was. It looked alien, like a black meteorite half-buried in the chalky soil of the South Downs. Three feet high, or more, its surface oddly bejewelled in black and grey. I thought of Superman's crashed spaceship. It sat in a rough circle of trampled grass, a clearing created by booted feet.

"Look."

Rory pointed at the side of the mass with his stick. It took me a moment to recognize what he was showing me. Four blocky silver letters embedded in the black: S-O-N-G. I scratched at my armpit. Rory looked at me expectantly, grinning that lopsided grin of his. He poked at it with the stick again.

"Song? What's that supposed to mean?"

I could see he wanted to laugh, but he resisted the urge to call me a retard.

"Not song. S-U-N-G. Samsung. It's a phone. They're all phones. Must be hundreds of them. Someone's been burning them."

Now that he'd said it I could see the curve of the U, the familiarity of the blocky font. Rory started poking around the edges of the circle, and after a few jabs with the stick he picked a small red matchbox out of the grass. He pushed it open, revealing seven or eight matches, all dry and unbroken, nestled together at one end. I sensed the spark in his grin, the mischievous swagger as he pocketed them. Our parents didn't allow matches in the camp. They said we had to learn how to start fires the old fashioned way, now that the phosphorus factories had closed down. The Event had changed everything. On his better days Dad would joke that the survivalists had been right all along.

As we walked away from the circle Rory bent a second time, plucking something bigger from inside a cluster of nettles. It looked like an old PlayStation Vita, the screen cracked from corner to corner. We still collected these trinkets of our past like they were shiny pebbles, telling ourselves that they might be worth something one day, when the lights came back on. After an experimental jab at the buttons he shrugged and pushed it into his backpack too.

***

We smelled them before we saw them. The odour was subtle at first, and Rory and I looked at each other slyly, wondering who was to blame. We'd been living on plundered cans of beans and corned beef since leaving the camp. It wasn't a diet that promoted digestive health. But as the smell grew stronger it became more suggestive of farms and livestock, of animals even sweatier and dirtier than us. After seven days on the path it felt like an omen of things to come.

I saw the dome of the first shelter before Rory did, a low curve of corrugated metal half-closed at one end to act as a makeshift door. As if someone had half-buried a metal pipe in the soft loam of the Downs. From a distance the scale wasn't clear, and my first thought was that someone was camping up there. By the time the third and fourth shelters were visible Rory had started to pay attention too, his nose raised as if he was sniffing the air, like a mongrel dog on alert. This was beginning to look like a settlement. We'd been trying to avoid groups of people whenever possible, but unless we slid down the slopes of the escarpment into the valley below there was no way around these strange, minimalist structures. Our pace slowed as more of them came into view. There were at least forty or fifty. Maybe a hundred.

It was only as we drew closer that the scale of them became clear. Unless their owners were the size of hobbits, these sheds didn't house people. We rounded a corner and saw the gate, and the barbed wire fences strung along either side of the path. Then, finally, the pigs.

Rory laughed. "I guess it's bacon for dinner, then."

The larger animals were confined to their pens by a system of wire fences and shallow ditches, but as we swung our legs over the gate three piglets raced across the path, squealing in alarm as they sought out their mothers. Legs scampering, snouts thrust upwards in a desperate bravado. It reminded me of our camp, the younger ones running wild while their parents wallowed in the doorways. An unexpected stab of longing hit me and I had to catch my breath.

Rory was already examining the fences, sending some of the pigs scattering while others eyed him with bemusement. The mud in the pens looked damp, as if it had been watered recently, but at the edges it was caked dry and crusty. Someone had raked in straw to hold it together. Rory rattled his stick along the wire as he walked.

"Whoever owns this place has a pretty good setup. They've been fed, you know. Which means someone is still running this as a farm. Can you imagine? The camp would die for a setup like this. I'm not sure I'd ever grow sick of pork chops for dinner."

"You'd be surprised."

We were used to our own company, so it took us a
moment to realize that neither of us had spoken. Rory raised
the stick in his fist. I took a step back, only stopping when my
heels ran up against the edge of a ditch. There was a pause. I
could feel my heart banging hard against my ribs, the sweat
tickling the back of my neck. The snuffling of the pigs grew
louder, as if they could sense a change, the muggy
forewarning of a storm.

Then a head rose above one of the sheds and he
stepped into view. He wasn't a tall man, barely a few inches
above Rory and myself, his shoulders curved in a tired slope.
I'd guess he was a little older than my Dad. His face was
brown, and dry like leather, and where he gripped the bucket
handle his knuckles looked red and chapped. His shirtsleeves
were rolled up past his elbows, revealing sinewy forearms
bristling with pale hairs. When he smiled it didn't look as if it
came naturally to him, the corners of his lean mouth being
tugged at unfamiliar angles.

"Don't worry," he bent slightly and the bucket
clattered to the straw-packed dirt, "I come in peace. Just
travelling through, are you? Heading on into Steyning?"

Rory lowered his stick slightly and looked across at
me. We hadn't known we were close to a village. It must be
hidden down in the valley somewhere. Our parents had
mentioned Steyning to us before. They'd heard reports from
the transients passing through our camp: stories of houses

173

burnt to the ground, mobs setting upon anyone suspected of harbouring the old technology. They blamed the old way of life for everything that had happened to us. That explained the burnt pyre we'd seen earlier on the trail.

"You're a quiet pair, aren't you. Have you come from further along the coast?"

Rory still didn't lower his stick completely, but I could see his shoulders relax. "We have. We've got people not far behind us, so you'd best not try anything funny."

"Of course you have. But the sun's going down in close to an hour, and unless you're heading into Steyning you'll want somewhere to stop for the night. I need to finish up here, but then you're welcome back at the house. No spare room unfortunately, but the barn is warm and clean. The straw's pretty comfy, too."

We glanced at each other again. Our backs were knotted from sleeping in the dirt the last few nights, our legs stiffening from the climb. We were safer facing one man than an entire mob.

"Plus, of course, I have pork chops for dinner."

I saw Rory smile.

***

He told us his name was Peter Faulkner, although everyone around these parts called him Pig Pete. The farm had already

been running for a few years when the disaster happened.
There had been some opposition when it first set up on the
hill, but that evaporated with the collapse of the old ways.
Since then the local villagers had come to depend on him for
their meat. It meant he could barter for anything he needed.
The farmhouse wasn't palatial but it was only Pete living
there, and he could get tinned goods, and sometimes fresh
vegetables. They let him be as long as he kept their larders
stocked with chops and bacon.

"I smoke it on the premises, see. Best you'll get around
these parts, before or after what happened."

Dinner was a plate heaped with two chops each, plus
several rashers of Pete's best bacon. The meaty smell rising
from it was enough to reignite our neglected appetites. He'd
cooked some cabbage on the side, but Rory and I left that until
last. I ate a little, so he wouldn't think we were ungrateful. He
still had running water, from a well out the back, and a wood-
fired stove that doubled as an oven. I could see Rory was
thinking the same thing as me: this was the best setup we'd
seen, inside or outside the camp.

We took turns in the bathroom, using the lukewarm
water to wash standing up in the bathtub. After a week on the
road the dirt had worked its way into the whorls of my
fingers, the hidden nooks in my ears. When the water swirled
away the bottom of the tub was still dusted with a fine grit.

While Rory took his turn I helped Pete dry and stack the plates. He kept looking out the window as we worked, his eyes restless. There was only silence outside in the dark, the occasional grunt or squeal from where the pig pens butted up against the barn. His nervousness was contagious, and I almost dropped one of the plates as he passed it to me.

"Careful with that. They used to be my mother's." His eyes strayed to the window again, then turned back to me. "There never were any others coming along behind you, were there? It's just you two boys out here alone?"

I looked in the direction of the bathroom. From the splashing sounds it would be a while before Rory had cleaned every dirt-filled crack.

"No. It's just us. Our camp's about a week away, although I expect some of them are trying to follow us."

"Runaways, are you?"

"I'm thirteen, you know. Rory's almost fourteen. We're old enough to be out here on our own. We can look after ourselves."

Pete chuckled. "I'm sure you can. Have you got anything to trade, though? If I'm giving you supper and bed, I mean. What's in it for me?"

There was a pause, and I could feel that the chemistry in the room had changed. There was something new between us, not quite a threat, but something clumsy and unpredictable. The pigs were his meal ticket, he was used to receiving something in return. I was standing close to the stove and could feel the heat of it against my leg, spreading up across my back and my neck like a sweat stain. Outside in the dark something squealed then fell silent.

I didn't hear Rory come in. Before I was fully aware of his presence he was speaking, pushing past me with his hand outstretched.

"What about this? We found it on the hillside. I know it doesn't work, but people still collect these, right? Someone will still trade it with you. It has value."

He was holding out the PS Vita, and for a second I thought I saw Pete recoil. He gathered himself quickly, gesturing with his hand that Rory should put it away.

"Don't let the villagers see that. These are changed times. I don't need it, and I recommend that you lose it soon. Does that mean you don't have anything else to offer?"

Rory dug around in his backpack. His hand emerged holding two tins of beans. It was what we'd have eaten for dinner anyway, so I figured it was as close to a fair trade as we could get. He didn't mention the box of matches. Pete shrugged and took them, stowing them in a high cupboard out of our reach. After the transaction he seemed quieter, almost ashamed. As he showed us out to the barn, and the straw pallets that would be our beds, I felt that he was about to apologise for something. But the apology never came, and after he closed the barn doors behind us we heard him coughing on his way back to the house.

The straw was soft, as he'd promised, although the dust tickled the back of my throat. I wanted to talk to Rory about Pete, and the sense I'd had that something wasn't quite right, but exhaustion surprised me with its persistence. I fought briefly with my eyelids, before surrendering to the cushion of sleep.

***

It was still dark when I woke. In those first few seconds of confusion I thought we were back in the camp, our parents arguing just beyond the door of my room. Then the smell of straw and pigs hit me. The voices came from outside the barn doors, and they were drawing closer. At least ten voices, all male.

Rory had always been a deep sleeper, so I rolled over and shook him awake. He was about to complain about the intrusion, but then he must have seen the panicked look on my face, because he stopped, mouth open. The voices were close now, rising above the grunting and squealing of the animals. I could hear a few words through the doors.

We could barely see anything in the dim light of the barn, but the slivers filtering through the cracks offered a little illumination. Our bags slung in the corner, Rory's shoes, the fuzzed outlines of the bales behind us. Rory moved before I did, grabbing a rake that was propped against the wall and sliding it through the door handles.

"Now at least they can't get in."

I was about to point out that we also couldn't get out when the doors shook, as if someone was ramming their shoulder against them. We heard a voice rise above the others, a deep, harsh voice that reminded me of a preacher, or a judge.

"We know you're in there. And we know what you have. Pig Pete has squealed." There was laughter. "Come out here and be judged like men."

I looked to Rory but he was already scrabbling over the straw to the back of the barn. I grabbed my bag and followed, feeling my way in the darkness. When we reached the back wall I saw what he'd been heading for: a small, square window that was partially hidden by the bales. It would be a drop of six feet or more down the other side. In the light from outside I could just see the white of Rory's grin.

"What? You didn't think I'd set up camp here without checking for the escape routes first, did you?"

The men were still shouting at the front of the barn, their voices rising as the preacher cursed and pounded on the door. We opened the window as quietly as we could and I squeezed through first. The landing was soft, the grass growing high against the wall. Now that I was outside I could hear the anger in the men's voices more clearly. Rory appeared at the window but before he swung out I saw him take the box of matches from his pocket. There was a flare of light, then a bigger flare as the entire box caught fire. His face was lit from below, a flicker of something like a smile passing across it, a hint of the wildness that we'd both felt since leaving home. As he jumped he tossed the matches behind him into the barn.

"That should keep them occupied for a while. Come on."

As we ran and slid down into the valley I glanced back. At first there was nothing, but soon we could see an orange glow, growing brighter as the sounds of alarm increased. Once we were far enough away, under cover of a small copse of trees, we stopped and watched. The barn was fully alight now, flames flickering through gaps in the walls. Thick, black smoke obscured the stars. After a few minutes I turned to walk away, but Rory held me back with his arm. The fire had reached out and caught hold of the straw dug into the dirt of the pig pens, the bales of kindling Pete had worked into the dust. In a matter of minutes the entire hilltop was ablaze, a golden crown of fire that engulfed the house, the barn, and the farm itself as it fed its hunger.

When we couldn't take any more we finally turned and walked away into the darkness, trying to ignore the heat at our backs. On the breeze came a hint of smoke, and, somewhere, the sound of distant squealing.

Man Who Talks to Books
Rachel J Fenton

That's what folk call me, among things; I don't so much talk as
hum. They used to call me flying man. They used to talk to
me. Now it's just books keeps me company. And magazines:
paragliding ones is what I like best, still counts as books far as
I'm concerned, but I'm not fussy. Halie said I am, but I
disagree. You don't get from North of England to Auckland's
North Shore, to spend ten of your fifty-odd years sleeping on
street, by being fussy. There's probably a book to prove it, in
science section, but I'm not moving from here to look for it.
I'm not moving unless I have to. I like this spot. End of
magazines rack by paragliding suits me. I do read other stuff,
believe me. I move when I have to. I move when librarian asks
me. But see, now you're thinking, he's fussy. Now you're
thinking, he only reads paragliding magazines, what does he
know about science? Well, aren't you? Here, then, just to
prove I read science, take this magazine: says here, scientists
want to use shark skin to coat outside of boats, make them go
faster. Under a microscope, skin is jagged scales; so rough,
bacteria can't grow there. Scientists also want to use that: fact.
Nothing at all to do with paragliding, that. Here's another fact:

they say, in paragliding, longer you do it, more likely you are to lose somebody you know. I don't disagree with that. What I disagree with is way folk go about telling me to move, get lost. Take this librarian doing rounds, giving it closing time. He won't say it to me; no one talks to my face. They think they don't have to; folk don't look at me; mams pulling bairns away, shush. But like I say, I'm not fussy. Drink anything, me. I got lost long before Halie told me to.

I like Takapuna library. It's warm when outside's cold. And in summer, there's air con. Having a lavvy to hand helps, an'all. Mostly librarians let me be. Mostly I keep to myself; crouch darn at end of magazine rack. Usually I occupy me-sen. Now and then there's something going on and I watch that, sometimes I can see it in gloss, if it's a new magazine, if cover's not obscured by too many fingerprints, creases or stains. Take two women dancing now at mouth of glass lift: I see it cough t'old lass out and swallow younger one as if it's happening in front of me. For a second, lift takes me with it, back, down; on magazine's cover, she's spit of Halie, hair so black it appears she's just crawled out of sea.

First time Halie spoke to me, in chip shop, last before path takes you up to whale bones in Whitby Bay, she called me a dog. I followed her round like one after that. I talked her into having a drink with me. I ate so many spuds that week and I must have had a trawler's worth of fish swirling in my belly, sick for her, I was. Bloody hell, she made me spin.

I turn to look at lift. There's a man fair galloping down stairs. Life's not a race. Easy enough to say when finish line's in sight, I suppose. What do I know? I'm just making life up. Only true things are what you read in books and I a'n't found me-sen inside one of you yet.

I get up, my knees are starting to ache anyway and kids are leaving with their homework. I can't bear it when they laugh. One little blinder stuck a blob of chewing gum on my back, one time. Imagine that, stuck it on like you would on wall of pub john. You have to have money to waste gum. All money and no manners round wealthy parts, not like when we first arrived, no such thing as a millionaire back then, not here. That's what I liked, what drew us to this place. A different pace is lie they use these days but for us, me and Halie, we needed a fresh start and she needed to be somewhere by sea. Well, me, I needed to be far away from her family, for a start, but, looking back, I suppose I thought I could get far away from me. Not so much a slow boat to China as a slow swim to bottom of world.

Now library's clearing, there's a newspaper free. I sit behind partition to read.

They sell babies in China, ground up in pills after they've been kilned. And a man got arrested in Thailand for smuggling a box with six foetuses in, all in various states of development, all covered in markings and gold leaf, all curled like ears but wonder who was listening like Minnie Dean as their last cries went out?

Minnie Dean was most famous baby killer to make New Zealand news. No one tattooed either of two found inside her hat tin. Good as gold, bet that's how she described them, over-lollied on laudanum – that's lettuce juice to me and thee – who knows? She was a Scots lass; ended up in Winton afore gallows. Must be something about Northern Hemisphere makes us want to get away, hit opposite, literally. Ah well, I went from a straight talking lover to a loner with my head in books, and now a newspaper, though you'd lure me out for a Scotch.

Downstairs I can hang about in poetry. They don't think to look for me here. Only trouble is, here I get a smell of café and it wakes my stomach up; there are some things I'd rather not feel. I run my finger over spines, reminds me of railings as a kid, few remaining from munitions raids; raids weren't for making tanks or bombs or whatnot at all but were just to boost morale. Imagine, being told to take away someone's security for good of their country's health.

Sh – commands: Shakespeare. Wh – questions: Whitman. Wo – *sadness:* Wordsworth.

They kicked me out for being too loud, that's how it gets me; I can't keep poisoner quiet.

Halie said drink was my true love. Not so, my dear, for love is silent assassin. You got me a direct hit, my darling. I fell like a stag. Not all one-sided, mind; when I asked her to marry me, I didn't know how not to. It only surprised me she said yes.

We got hitched in Sheffield town hall. Her mother came down from Whitby on train, but her old dad stayed behind counter of chippie, sent only a prophecy it wouldn't last, could tell us exact number of years we had left. Silly bugger, shame he couldn't foresee end of his days coming up to bite him in ticker.

Honeymoon weekend, I took her to Runswick, gave her mother a lift back en route. We camped, snug in our tent as Hobbs famed in that bay, in spite of air mat being flat and embarrassment of having to ask round campsite for loan of a foot-pump. I dug boats in sand and Halie sat between my knees while I paddled us metaphorically out to sea. She said I'd make a great dad. What dreams we had.

Walking back to tent that night, I sprained my foot, shouted at her for laughing. My bark's worse than my bite, do you see? Sulked, surrounded by cast-offs of smaller birds, shells of whelks.

We drove back to my place in Sheffield in silence, an hour moving nowhere on A1, headlight to tail, while storm clouds grew high above before letting force of anvil fall as I unpacked boot. I slept in car that night. Next day, I bought her an angel, only a piece of pot but she loved it to bits, she did, aye, collected them after that.

I don't remember how I got here. Sunnynook Park, it's a good name; it fits.

Librarians wouldn't mind so much if I didn't speak, they assume rightly it's drink, not that I can't keep my thoughts in my head, I only talk when one looks like they want to be my friend, out loud, to books, keep them from getting too close. Most folk assume I don't care that I stink, assume I've given up. That's where they're wrong, where we're all wrong about drink: it only makes me care more. They call me man who talks to books. I used to be flying man. One day I'll end up in sea, go full circle, back to my roots.

In grass growing through bottom of this recycling cage is biggest cricket I've ever seen.

~~~

Up in air over Castleton, cement chimney is needle for only compass I need. Ring ousel call – a chirrup like crickets – heard as I dip low over Stanage Edge, headed towards Millstones, Toad, Robin Hood's Cave, flying in circles, chasing crows. All climbers are out in Joe Simpson's playground. A couple of hikers wave at me. *Trouble with doing something right first time is that nobody appreciates how difficult it was.* Walter J West said that. Just goes to show how perfect conditions can be, so that seeing your best mate corkscrew into heather in sight of Right Unconquerable, hearing his vertebrae break

THE LONELY CROWD - ISSUE ONE

startles itself into memory with most beautiful of things. In this way, everything of beauty takes on board tragedy and everyone you love sinks in your sadness. This is when drinking starts.

~~~

Folk round here are more considerate than on sea front, put their rubbish in bins; cans go in this cage, through a tilting slide in top like a laundry-shoot-type thing. It looks like kind they take in sea to photograph sharks; sort poor buggers in Hong Kong live in; sort battery hens go through. They throw them out, too, when they can't lay eggs anymore, when they can't go any faster.

Jack and Jill, at it like a jigger till booze set in. There are many ways to lose it. Nobody ever tells you that, nobody warns you poison gets into your wood.

Trouble had started before move; emigrating was meant to be our escape. We were meant to start a family. It has to be hard to do that. Maybe it's payback; been killing my family since I were a lad.

We used to sabre cow parsley with a stick of birch. I made some cracking pea shooters from dead stems, hawthorn agars as peas. One time I urged my sister Anne to take a bunch of cow parsley flowers inside for our mam. Got her a hiding that did; came out with wet tracks burning her cheeks, hair full of lace like an angry bride, she was. Years later, she told me, after she lost bairn, what our mother had said to her, how she'd given her Queen Anne's curse. She really believed that, lost her brain, hasn't spoken to me since.

Don't make an enemy of your sister.

Little lass gives me daggers; beautiful eyes. Her mam must be hurting her hand, knuckles going white where she's clutching, pushing bairn along on plastic trike. They stop at climbing frame, and a toddler, a little lad takes up where girl's mam left off and pushes her full pelt. Little lass is screeching like a barn owl in Dolby stereo, *eek*, wheeling faster than she's ever gone in her life. I'd love to see look she gives him when he's done. Girl's mother's intercepting poor bugger now, tells him to let go. What's betting he's wondering why they gave her wheels in first place?

Over road by acupuncture place there's an old girl wearing a surgical mask, scared to death of catching bird flu, it's a wonder she's outside. Travel twelve thousand miles to spend your life in a room identical to one you left. May as well have stayed put and brought outside in your head.

Hindsight's a marvellous thing, blinding hell fire, in't it just?

I'm just another drunk with no family, nowt to leave behind, not even a book with my name on it. There were some notable literary drunks: Ernest Hemingway, James Baldwin and Jack Kerouac to name but three. Not me.

They used to call me flying man. Like gulls: these don't fuss, too well fed for fighting, not like scrappers of Whitby and Runswick Bay. If I had wings again, mine would be made of shark skin. I'd glide so fast shit could never stick. Folk would write about me, redeem me, in books: poems, stuff of folk songs. *Like a drunk in a midnight choir, I have tried in my way to be free.*

The Book of Job[1]

Bethany W Pope

'Why do the righteous suffer?' Job asked God.
'Everyone says I deserve this devilment,
And I know that I don't.' He scratched his wounds,
Received no answer. He had to wait until the fall.
Eventually, God spoke to the man whose house
And life He'd broken. God spoke to Job in the flesh.

Now, in the beginning, things were different; Job's
flesh,
Opulent and smooth: he was rich. Job thanked God
Very early in the morning when his house
Exhaled the sweet sleep-breath of his children and the
Devil
Loitered far away. Job rose from his bed, fell
To his knees and gave thanks in his room. He wound
His Tefillin around his arm and forehead, God's words
wound,

---

[1] This is an acrostic sestina crown. The acrostic reads, 'We are a novel that
God is writing. We suffer for the sake of His plot, for the glory of the Artist.
We are characters who must agonize in order to grow. The devil's a plot
device. Evil is an evolutionary spur. Goodness is the fruit of woe. Our pain
makes us interesting to God. Our pain makes us real. One day we will be
real enough to step off the page.'

A leather-bound remembrance of His mercy towards
flesh.

Thinking, 'These aromatic cedar walls could never fall.

God is good and shall preserve them. My God

Observes my charity. I feed beggars and devil-

Destroyed men, haunted by grief. They enter my
house;

I care for them. Parentless children are welcome in my
house

So that they will not starve on the street. I wash their
wounds

With oil and water so that the Devil

Retreats without planting infection in their flesh.

I do my best to be worthy of God.'

These pleasant thoughts interrupted his prayers. He
fell

Into self-congratulation. He fell

Never noticing the plummet. Inside his house

Grand tapestries told the stories of God:

Wandering Israelites sewn onto a silken desert,
wounds

Embroidered in red dye extracted from crushed flesh,

Strained from the bodies of insects. The Devil

Understood. He knows our nature. The Devil

Fell a long time ago. In the beginning, he fell,

Free and burning, wings scorched to ashes against his
flesh.
'Everyone so well cared for, everyone whose house
Returns such riches, can praise you, Lord. Wounds
Fester and burn. Injure him and he'll curse his God.'
'Open the cask of misery upon him, Devil,' God
Replied, 'Fell his house. Slaughter his children.
Though you wound his flesh, still he shall praise me.'

How quickly lives can fall apart, when God
Extends a wager! As soon as he could, the Devil
Struck down all of Job's cattle. Festering wounds
And parasitic worms ate them, inside and out. They
fell,
Kicking thick dust with their hooves as they died. The
house
Exploded with activity, hustling to save whatever flesh
Open sores had not yet bloomed on. Most of the cow-
flesh,
Foul to every sense, was spoiled, but God
Has his requirements. Job sent a clean calf to the
priest's house.
It was his last healthy animal. The Devil
Sputtered with laughter as Job slit its white throat. It
fell,

Painting its blood on the high stone altar. Its wound
Leered open: an ill-willed grin. Its death was a wound
On the face of Job's faith – but he believed he owed this
flesh
To God, not in payment for riches or safety from falls.
'From my mother's womb, I emerged naked. God
Ordered the cells of my body, the hairs on my head.
Devils
Refuse to give thanks. I'm not owed anything. This
house,
Tight-caulked, richly furnished, remains only a house.
High walls are no protection from Fate. We will be
wounded,
Exactly as we must be.' This speech left the Devil
Grinning with a bitter joy. 'The fruit of his flesh,
Love's brightest produce, I'll take next – in the name of
God.'
Over the bedrooms of Job's children, Satan's shadow
fell,
Reaching in through their windows. He took them.
Pulses fell,
Youthful faces blanched with ageing illness. The house,
Overcome by Death, fell silent and cold. 'Oh God,
Forgive my husband for his sins!' Job's wife cried. She
wound

Tight white cloths around the bodies, the stiffening
flesh
Her children had become. She said, 'You are the Devil.
Each child was more precious than incense and the
Devil
Arrived and stole off with their souls.' She fell,
Rigid as a day-old corpse, into her bed. Her flesh
Tried to join her children in death. 'This house
Is too empty. My heart is a wound.'
She lay, pale and still. In her heart, she cursed God.
The way of all flesh is suffering. No house protects
from
Wounds, or the Devil. Everything falls into loss.
Each person on earth owes God one death.

Awakened in the dead of night by smoke, God's
Radiant light – or an inferno ignited by the Devil –
Everything around Job blossomed with fire-flowers.
His wounded,
Crying wife gasped as they groped to the window.
They fell,
Hard, onto the packed-soil foundation of the house
And lay there, smothered in sweet cedar smoke. Job's
flesh
Reddened, cracked; his face blistered as he cooked.
Flesh

And blood can only survive so much torment. 'Oh God,'

Cried Job, 'Why won't you help me? You've turned my house

To tinder. It smoulders like the throne of the Devil.

Everything is lost to me.' Job's wife was injured in her fall.

Ribs splintered. Her lungs were pierced and she died, wounded,

Sobbing curses at God with lips that bubbled blood. Her wounds

Went deeper than mere insult to flesh.

How can anyone live without hope? Fall

Out of your secure nest and die like an ill-fledged bird. God

Must watch the sparrow, yes, but He need not help. The Devil

Understands this. Our broken bones decorate his house.

She was buried by Job, beneath the ashes of their house.

The still-warm pile served as Job's mattress. His wounds

All festered in the filth, sores oozing like the eyes of the Devil.

God looked on, with interest; fascinated by this flesh.

One day, then another passed. Job still praised God,
Naked as Adam after the fall.
Isolated by friends (they tend to falter, after you fall -
Zealots dedicated to avoiding ill-fortune), his house
Existed only in memory, but, 'God
Is good.' Job said, 'He owes me nothing. I am wounded
Now, but I have been blessed.' Job's delicate flesh
Overran with leaking cracks. Broken skin tempted the
Devil.
Righteousness is catnip to The Accuser. The Devil
Delighted in breaking Job down. 'I'll make him fall.
Every moment until then shall be my pleasure. His
flesh,
Raw as it is, still feels pain. In my house
There are many weapons, many methods of
wounding.'
Outside of it all, watching, creating, the author – God.
God seems a cold, indifferent creator. Our flesh fails,
Riches fall away from us; the Devil consumes
Our houses and wounds our spirits – savouring our
loss.

When the sun rose, the landscape blazed with the
beauty of God,
The figs and olives glistened with dew. The Devil

Held his head in agony of thought, 'I made wet
wounds
Erupt across his haunches, his hair has bleached and
fallen,
Deep cracks in his feet weep blood and fleas call him
their home.
Enterprising jiggers have gnawed into the soft fleshy
Veins between his toes. Every inch of his flesh
Is inflamed, in agony, yet I am still losing my bet with
God.'
Lucifer plotted, then flew to a house
Several miles from the ruins that devilled
Aching Job. Zophar sat outside, watching animals fall,
Placing bets with Elphaz and Bildad over which
wounded
Lion would win the fight they forced. The big cats were
wounded,
Overcome by exhaustion as they clawed each other's
flesh,
Tearing their way out of the fighting-pit over the fallen,
Draggled corpses of previous competitors. The God-
Enforcer flayed them with whips whenever they
paused. The Devil
Veritably chortled at such sweet sport. 'This house
Is perfect for my needs,' he said. 'This palace houses

Ceaseless misery – men who know exactly how to
wound.

Exquisite torturers who do not know that they devil

Everyone.' Satan transformed. He borrowed the flesh

(Very fine, too) of a rich merchant, a man blessed by
God.

'I've come to enlist your help,' said Satan, 'A great man
has fallen.

Loath I am to say it, but it's Job that's taken a fell

Injury. His fortune is lost, his house:

Smouldering ruins. His wife, and his children, have
gone to God.

A good man is in need of friends and comforters to
tend his wounds.'

No one likes to imagine themselves hard-hearted.
Their flesh

Exhibited the symptoms of grief. They thought they
felt it. The Devil,

Very subtly, enabled hypocrisy. 'What the Devil

Ordained, man can undo!' ejaculated Bildad. 'The fell

Luck surrounding our friend shall be dispersed.' Red
fleshed,

Urgently trembling, the sportsmen packed bags and
fled their house

To bring food and aid to a man badly wounded.

In the ashes, Job sat, scratching himself and praying to
God.
'Oh Lord, why have you forsaken this wounded flesh?
No fall would slay me, no devil torment, if you
Answered me. God, your mercy is my only home!'

Returning to consciousness after weeping to God,
Yearning for a clay cup of cool water to ease the
devilish
Scratch in his throat and pour onto his crusted wounds
(Pus itches badly) Job looked up and saw ashes falling
Under a sky, crystalline and blue. His house,
Ruins now, flavoured the air with cedar and burnt
flesh,
Greasy and sweet: his wife's fat and flesh,
Odorous, cooked by the coals. 'Why did God
Ordain this?' he wondered, dry-swallowing atoms of
his home,
Dust caking his larynx. 'I'm haunted by a devil.'
Near evening, his would-be friends arrived. They fell,
Embracing him. They poured wine and passed beef-
strips, wound
String-like around long batons of bread. 'Wounds
So serious need careful tending.' Zophar said, 'Your
flesh

Is so damaged, so delicate, it will fall,
Sloughing off, at the slightest touch.' He grimaced,
'God
Tends to the good and abandons the wicked to the
Devil.
How did you wind up in his bad books? My house
Expands every day. I must be pleasing him. Your
house
Flared up in a blaze and is gone for good.' Job's smile, a
wound,
Running bloody across his face, became a mask of the
Devil.
Until this moment, he had not known that his
weakened flesh,
Isolated state, and endless sorrow (allowed by God)
Transmitted the idea to these men that he had earned
his fall.
'Of course you must have done something, ' Elphaz
added, 'to fall
Far and fast. We may not feed the hungry in my house,
We may do a little healthy gambling, but God
Observes and approves. You must have earned your
wounds
Enjoying something awful.' He blushed, 'Was it boy-
flesh,

Or the tender assholes of women that led you to the
Devil?'
Urgently, Job stood. He shrieked like the Devil,
'Return to whatever sewer-pit you crawled from. The
fell
Pleasures you describe mean nothing to me. My flesh,
Angry as it is, has done nothing to deserve becoming a
house
Infested with infection. Sometimes, the people God
wounds
Never deserve it. Maybe it's sport to God.
Maybe my wounded flesh is nothing more than
An angry God's weekend entertainment, but no fall is
random. I
Know that even the Devil serves in the Master's home.'

Escaping this haranguing, Job's false friends fled. God
Saw what happened to them. I won't record it. The
Devil
Understood that he was losing, but he knew that some
wounds
Seem staunched right before they explode. The fall
Is always harder for those higher on the wall. Houses
Never seemed to matter much, until Job lost his. His
flesh

Tightened as his pustules swelled. The soft, fleshy

Exoskeletons of jiggers burned between his toes. 'Oh God,

Return and answer me! Why did you destroy my house,

Ensnare my children and feed my body to the Devil?

See, I stand before you, naked in my fall.

Take pity, O Lord, and give me answer for my wounds.'

In an instant, the clear sky clouded over: sand rose and wound

Nebulous spirals of grit; beauty, flesh-

gouging and terrible, a diamond sea that would not fall.

The Whirlwind spoke in the glassy voice of God,

Opening the earth in fissures deep enough to bury the Devil.

God spoke, 'Who darkens counsel without knowledge? What house

Or stall gave rise to such an ignorant voice? This little home,

Delicate planet, was woven for my pleasure. Each wound:

Ordained by my words, according to plan. No devil

Undermines my purpose, no mere creature of flesh

Refuses my Plot, for I am the Lord God,

Poet of the universe, opener of the ragged gates of death. You fell

And praised me. Good. Out of my womb fell

Ice and fire, glacier and volcano. My loins beget the dew. My house

Never reaches completion, my plants never fail in their fruit. God

Made you, man, to praise Him. So praise Me in your wounds

And know that only when you've been broken in your flesh,

Keening and scarred, once you've suffered more than the Devil

(Expert as he is) could engineer, could you rise higher than the Devil,

See farther than your pain, and hear My voice.' Job fell

Under the weight of his terror, his flesh

Succumbing to pain and fear. He fainted into the ashes of his house.

Relief flooded his body, a cool wind caressing his wounds,

Easing his agony. The wind whispered in the voice of God.

As the night passed, Job's wounded flesh scabbed. The scabs

Loosened, and fell; new skin itching like the devil. God

Opened the gates to His house (the heavens) and a
cleansing rain fell.

Now, in the land of Uz there lived a man who spoke
with God,
Escaped a state like hell, and beat the gambling Devil.
Destruction left him battered, covered in wounds,
Alone, but it could not break his spirit or force him to
fall.
Years passed, as they always do. Job rebuilt his house,
Worked his land hard and traded wine-grapes for cow-
flesh.
Each day, spent in the dust, brought prosperity closer.
Flesh
Wealed over, scars formed over sores, and God
Increasingly blessed Job's second try at a making a
home.
Love entered in the body of a woman (with eyes like
the Devil's),
Little children followed, one by one, falling
Between the soft amber legs of his wife: her womb-
wound.
Each child was precious, but could not heal the wound
(Re-lived every day) left by Job's first family. The flesh
Erases injury – not so the soul. Job's first fall

Ached. Still, he gave his time and money, built a
temple for God;
Long, white blocks of marble for the altar. The Devil,
Embarrassed, never tormented him again. Job's house,
New-built, smelled of incense and cedar. This house
Overflowed with silks, fruits and skins of fine wine.
Vines wound
Under the rafters and Job's children made faces,
mocking the Devil,
Gurning and grinning like gargoyles between the
fleshy,
Health-giving bunches of grapes. So, Job praised his
God,
Thanking him for the privilege of living, awaiting the
fall
(Overwhelming and fast) that comes for us all. This fall
Seems random. It isn't. Rich or poor, every house
That mankind builds, every little life, belongs to God.
Expect no more than any other written character. You'll
be wounded:
Poetry's plot requires action. Your tender flesh
(Over brittle bones) supplies the drama. The Devil's
Fifth Business: forcing action. Job's children were small
devils,
Father's pride and joy, allaying nightmares from before
the fall

That led to their creation; their turn in the flesh.

How happily they played, in ignorance; running
through their house,

Evading capture. How easy they were to wound.

Pain forces us to grow, to become interesting. God

Allows the Devil to antagonize us, so that we fall,

Gored and wounded in flesh, and rise, with something
to say, into the

Embrace of God who waits to welcome us home.

In My Father's Garden
Gregory Norminton

HOME » GARDENING » GARDENS TO VISIT

Little Spinney

Ken Godfrey remembers the creator of an eccentric and enchanting garden.

It was with great sadness that I learned this week of the death of Gerald Surfleet, the celebrated Harley Street doctor and biographer of Andrew Marvell. With his ripe wit, sporting talent and extensive wine cellar, he was a good person to count as a friend. I will remember him best for his idiosyncratic contribution to English gardening.

Amidst the heaths, pines and executive houses of east Berkshire, Gerald Surfleet created Little Spinney: four acres of pure fantasy, divided into nine garden rooms, each inspired by a stanza from Marvell's poem 'The Garden'. These included a rill garden, a knot garden and an orchard stocked with ancient English apple varieties.

I remember visiting the scrubby wilderness – a great tangle of brambles and gorse, loud with the shrieking of children – when Surfleet was pegging out his future legacy. The early years were a riot of colour: asters and aquilegias, foaming borders of phlox and, in late summer, fireworks of agapanthus. Surfleet imposed a superstructure of topiaries and yew, with areas of paving and formal water. Follies began to creep in: the odd Grecian urn, an obelisk, a copy of a Roman bath spilling over with poppies. Surfleet had an artificer's knack for creating illusions, leading the visitor along suggestive, winding paths. In the early nineties, he extended the garden when he bought a neighbour's smallholding. There, where prosaic marrows had fattened, he created his loveliest spaces: the canal and sundial gardens and an azalea punchbowl.

My friend paid a high price for his devotion to horticulture, his wife, the actress Heda Surfleet, leaving him in 1980 and taking his two children with her. Yet I never heard Gerald complain about his loss. Perhaps it suited him to wander solitary in his creation. As Marvell wrote, "Two paradises 'twere in one / To live in paradise alone."

He was not alone for long, however, as a growing number of enthusiasts began to visit the garden, enchanted by its chromatic palette. The highlight, in the nineties, was a dazzling array of asters, eclipsed in the new millennium by an enviable collection of Victorian roses. Yet the garden was more than the sum of its parts. It was constantly evolving, a horticultural daydream, with unfamiliar vistas and fresh curiosities revealing themselves at each visit.

It is hard to believe, given the vigour of the man, that Gerald Surfleet is no more. He left us too soon, but did so with the knowledge that his legacy is secure. A five-person trust, including his son who inherits the house, will oversee the preservation of Little Spinney for generations to come.

*　　*　　*　　*　　*

Hi Nick. Looked for you in the nursery. Hope this finds you. The plants I require: wall germander, thyme, green sage, marjoram, myrtle, *lavandula x intermedia.* Can you get your hands on plenty of broken terracotta?

Best to you & Helen.

Mark S.

℘

To: Hugo Pickthorn, Andy Coates, Victoria Beazley

210

Subject: A knotty question!

Dear fellow trustees,

For reasons that will become obvious, I have not used our Google Group address for this email. It gives me no pleasure to be surreptitious, but given recent behaviour from Mark, I think it better to be discrete. I am sure it cannot have escaped your attention that the knot garden at Little Spinney has been tampered with. Actually, tampering is an understatement: I walked there yesterday and saw to my dismay that one of the knots has been dug up completely! The bare earth was quite a shock. I am certain that the box showed no sign of disease. Hugo, might you have a word? After my recent exchange with Mark, I feel a polite but firm letter from the chair would have more effect.

Wishing you all a very pleasant Bank Holiday weekend,

Marjorie

෴

Dear Hugo. Thanks for your letter. Rest assured that the knot garden is safe. I'm making it more authentic. *Buxus sempervirens* was an innovation of the C18th & pebbles for the unplanted spaces = anachronistic. With new planting and terracotta, I am adding a sense of history & aroma. Best wishes, Mark

P.S. Hope you like the saucy postcard. From Dad's collection of Donald McGills.

ဆ

To: Hugo Pickthorn, Andy Coates, Victoria Beazley
Subject: More innovations

Dear fellow trustees,

I went this morning to check on the 'progress' of the knot garden. I was reassured to a degree: the pattern has been restored, although I preferred the clipped box to Mark's amalgam of aromatics. I do wonder whether our acceptance of these changes is in keeping with our obligations to the Trust.

I should like to draw your attention to another development at Little Spinney. You may have noticed the proliferation of log piles. I know very well what purpose these serve, but while beetles may like them, garden enthusiasts are liable to find them unsightly and out of keeping with Little Spinney's character.

I spoke to Tom Atkins about his work under the new regime. He was loath to complain, but did mention the challenge of maintaining the garden without chemical fertiliser. There are certain areas for which Mark shows no enthusiasm: he is, for instance, 'not that fussed' (his words, apparently) about his father's roses. Consequently, the labour of manuring them falls exclusively to Tom. This, it seems to me, is no way to reward him for his decades of loyal service.

Yours in concern,

Marjorie

ဆ

To: Nick Haggerty
Subject: Fancy some topsoil?

Hi Nick, please find my shopping list attached. I plan to restore heather to Little Spinney. As for the lawns, time to put them back in nature's hands. I'll be selling topsoil if you've a use for it. Maybe we could do a trade. I need plenty of wildflower seed.

Must dash: I have a man coming round who collects smut.

Regards to Helen.

Mark

ℬℴ

To: Hugo Pickthorn, Andy Coates, Victoria Beazley
Subject: Upping our game

Dear fellow trustees,

I am writing this in the early hours of the morning, as I am quite incapable of sleep. Yesterday, I spent several hours in Little Spinney. I found brambles bursting out of the yew hedges and dragging at the azaleas. Many of the flowerbeds have been given over to nettles and dandelions. The urns are succumbing to goosegrass and the obelisk is disappearing under ivy. As for the orchard, it is in a lamentable condition, with great carpets mouldering over the grass. Tom Atkins tells me that this eyesore is part of a plan to turn the orchard into a 'forest garden'. Tom further informs me that there are plans afoot to close off two paths and to block up the view from the rill garden to the farmhouse. It is in reaction to these developments that I have seen fit to write to Mark Surfleet. Please find a copy of my letter in the attachment.

Yours as ever,

Marjorie

∽

To: M.Truscott@yahoo.co.uk
CC: little-spinney-trustees@googlegroups.com
Subject: Various

Dear Marjorie,

Thank you for your letter. I hope you won't mind my responding electronically: I am of that generation which finds it hard to think when writing by hand. Also, as you will appreciate, the disposal of my father's library (did he ever show you round, I wonder?) is taking up a great deal of my time, and I can type faster than I can scrawl.

I appreciate the sincerity with which you express your concerns about alterations at Little Spinney. However, I must say that I find some of your observations a little excessive. I have not allowed nettles and brambles to 'run rampant' through the azalea garden, but nettles are a major food plant for butterflies and so I tolerate them where I can. As for brambles, there were swathes of them on the land when I was a child, before my mother took us to Scotland. I am partial, aren't you, to blackberry jam.

You complain about my 'new regime' of low maintenance, but I think my father was a little too free in his use of glyphosate and difenoconazole. I suppose it was understandable, given his profession, that he saw fit to drug the gardens. This summer I predict fewer algal blooms in the canals: a direct result of the decline in nitrates. I consider a resident frog or palmate newt to be a greater ornament to Little Spinney than swathes of chemically doped flowers.

Elsewhere in your letter, you complain that I have let the cypresses grow too high in the sundial garden. I agree, which is why I plan to remove them before they plunge the site into shadow. As for the obelisk, ivy is indeed climbing up it. I do not see this as anything more than the monument's 'bedding in' to its setting. As you, of all people, must know, Dad liked a picturesque ruin.

You raise two final questions, which I can answer quickly. Tom is getting close to retirement age. I do not want to encumber him with too many tasks, and we have to work within budget. And no, I will not be 'channelling the proceeds' from the sale of my father's library and cellar into the maintenance of the garden. The terms of the Will were perfectly clear: the garden is in trust, the house and contents are my and my sister's inheritance.

With best wishes,

Mark

P.S. I did not know that the pebbles had been your gift to Dad. I have them in a bucket: do come and collect them if you want.

℘

To: Hugo Pickthorn, Andy Coates, Victoria Beazley
Subject: [No Subject]

Dear all,

I see from my inbox that you have received a copy of the outrageous letter addressed to me by Mark Surfleet. He has spared me the task of forwarding you the same. I shall not comment on his dismissive and patronising attitude towards me personally. It is my hope that his letter will finally persuade you about the approach he plans to take to his father's legacy – and to those of us entrusted with maintaining it.

Marjorie

இ

Little Spinney, 14th August

Dear Connie,

Happy anniversary to you and Ella! I've been imagining your celebratory picnic beside the lake. I hope the heat is less intense. Grim to think of Ottawa's forests going up in smoke.

Summer in England has been a more temperate affair: none of the droughts or floods of recent years. This is just as well, as Little Spinney in its present form is an unmanageable confection. It would be interesting – a Lord of Misrule summer – to let the vegetables come into flower and the wildlings sprout in the orchard. Why not let the self-willed seedlings put on their display, the poppies and foxgloves that Dad approved of so long as (like us) they knew their place. I find them more engaging than his collection of roses: fussy cultivars with scarcely a bee between them.

Speaking of Dad's collections, I've finally off-loaded his vintage erotica. Got a good price for it, which almost surprised me, given the infinite filth available to us on the Internet. I also had a valuer from Christie's take a look at the vases. They are seriously out of fashion, so maybe we should hold on to them until the winds of bad taste change.

Not much news otherwise. I rarely hear from Kathy, who's in New Zealand, probably in the arms of some vowel-warping Kiwi, and good luck to her. Been seeing a bit of Andy Coates. Had no idea he was so bitter about the loss of his land. We raided the cellar together and began to reminisce about the old days. I may have made some intemperate remarks, as by nightfall he was furiously convinced that Dad had played a part in the hiking of his ground rent. It is true that he was well connected: who knows what agreement might have been made on the golf course? Naturally, I tried to talk Andy down. He's a good bloke, but fouled up by life's disappointments.

This morning I saw a mole cross the cinder path. I stared after it – such an improbable sight, the half-blind lozenge of fur skittering out of its element until it found shelter under the yew – and I thought, Dad would have killed that little battler for the sake of his lawn.

Wishing you and Ella another year of happiness.

All my love,

M xx

P.S. Guess who's been dogging my every move. The other day, Marjorie Truscott battled through buddleia to warn me that, "at the current rate of decline, we will be dropped from the Yellow Book". I had to fight the urge to lift my hands to my face in pantomime horror.

P.P.S. Sorry about the crabbed handwriting. Too many days squeezing secateurs (not a euphemism).

ℰℴ

To: Hugo Pickthorn, Victoria Beazley
Subject: Andy's resignation

Dear Hugo and Victoria,

I must confess my dismay, not only at Andy's resignation from the board, but at the language he used to announce it. His absurd allegations concerning Dr Surfleet and myself I am prepared to overlook, but his maligning of the good doctor was outrageous, given the kindness that our late friend showed when he bought Andy's smallholding. Naturally, I do not wish to cast aspersions, but it cannot be a coincidence that Andy and Mark Surfleet can regularly be seen together propping up the bar at The Queens Oak.

Well, the Trust's work must continue. I look forward to continuing with the two of you in the years ahead.

Yours as ever,

Marjorie

ℰↄ

Peebles, 9th October

Dear Connie,

Thanks for your letter. I'm *delighted* that you and Ella have decided to become parents! Mum would be so proud of you. I certainly am.

Compared with your news, mine is trivial. Redecoration at the farmhouse continues. You would approve of my fetish for Farrow & Ball. The trustees still distrust me. I had Vicky Beazley over for tea, attempting an intervention. It was all rather half-hearted on her part. I could see her scoping out the changes to Dad's decor. Half expected her to take a nostalgic glance at his bedroom, but she fought the urge and took tea with me in the orangery, where I explained my vision for Little Spinney. Colonel Pickthorn remains more circumspect. He's a dutiful old duffer, stands ramrod straight when we meet – at attention – though I know his heart is in bad shape and he pants when we make our way about the garden.

My chief antagonist remains Marjorie T. I doubt she has much else to do with her time. She's the kind of woman who writes birthday cards to herself addressed from her cat.

I wonder if there's a romantic dimension to her obsession. It is possible, isn't it, that Dad in his dotage had to lower his erotic standards. Who's to say he didn't settle for that horse's arse?

Ouch – just slapped my wrist on your behalf.

Sorry for the short letter. I just wanted to write "Whoopee!" at the prospect of becoming an uncle.

Love to you, Ella, and the zygote.

M xx

೫

Contact Us Form

Your Details

Title*   Ms
First Name*   Marjorie
Last Name*   Truscott
Email*   M.Truscott@yahoo.co.uk

Address Line 1*	Cherry Tree Cottage
Address Line 2	Longwater Lane
Address Line 3	Finchampstead
Postcode*	RG40 4NX

Are you a subscriber to   Yes ⊙ No ○
The Daily Telegraph and
Sunday Telegraph
newspapers?

Your Enquiry

What does your   Other
enquiry relate to?*

Your enquiry   I have a story - rather a scoop - about a
garden, open to the public and in the
NGS Yellow Book, which is under threat
from a vengeful inheritor. I wish to write
in greater depth to your gardening
correspondent Ken Godfrey, who I
believe knew the garden's creator. I
would greatly appreciate it if you could
pass this message on.

ɛɔ

To: Nick Haggerty
Subject: Season of lists

Hi Nick,

Please find attached a hefty list of bulbs, saplings and seed for winter. It's going to be a busy planting season! Hope you approve of the apple and pear varieties – worthy replacements for the ornamental cherries and their meretricious blossoms.

I'm sorry that Marjorie Truscott has been harassing you about supplying Little Spinney. I have told her that Dad's old stockist was overcharging, but to no effect. She views every innovation as a betrayal.

Best, as ever, to you and H.

Mark

ɛɔ

To: Hugo Pickthorn, Victoria Beazley
BC: k.godfrey@telegraph.co.uk
Subject: Urgent

Dear Hugo and Victoria,

It seems our efforts to rescue the paths through the canal and sundial gardens have failed. Both have now been shut off with fencing and hedgerow saplings quite inappropriately planted to justify the enclosure. I have also discovered that, despite assurances, work has begun to brick up the view of the farmhouse from the rill garden. These developments are as nothing, however, to my final discovery. Tom Atkins had warned me of plans to replace the ornamental cherries, but nothing could have prepared me for the shock of finding the entire avenue destroyed. I telephoned M.S. to protest and his only response was that 'the trees will grow back'. Yes, but they will not be Gerald's!

I understand that you have attempted individually to reason with M.S. He can be a very persuasive and charming young man when it suits him. I have little doubt that he is endeavouring to break up the Trust, and to rid himself of all hindrances to his ambitions for Little Spinney. We must not let him succeed.

I would appreciate it if you could respond to this email as quickly as possible.

Marjorie

ℬ

To: Marjorie Truscott
CC: little-spinney-trustees@googlegroups.com
Subject: Under investigation

Dear Marjorie,

I know that we do not agree on all aspects of gardening. I regret that I spoke harshly to you on the telephone. Neither of these things justifies your subjecting me to investigation by a journalist. You will appreciate that it came as something of a surprise to find one trespassing on my driveway. What followed I can only describe as an interrogation. He said you accused me of 'infesting' Little Spinney with bees. Of course I regret what happened to your niece, but such is nature. Surely, as a gardener, you must recognise the vital role played by pollinators. As for the other accusations, I shan't bother to list them all, but I will tell you this: if my sister and I have any interest or expertise in gardening, it is entirely the result of our mother's example and not our father's. Finally, let me assure you that I have not 'hounded' Tom out of Little Spinney. The man is perfectly entitled to his retirement. I will of course miss his help and expertise, but with conservation volunteers stepping in at the weekends, I am confident we will be able to manage the land.

Yours, *etc.*

Mark Surfleet

ॐ

To: Victoria Beazley
BC: k.godfrey@telegraph.co.uk
Subject: Duplicity

Dear Victoria,

I resent your suggestion that I am being paranoid. Before his death, Gerald confided in me about his ex-wife and her manipulative ways. Heda was quite capable of appearing the victim of an injustice when she was its perpetrator: she was, after all, an actress. It seems plausible that these tendencies were passed on to her children. Given that M.S. inherited his father's charm, why should he not also have inherited his mother's duplicity?

Yours as ever,

Marjorie

꿍

Dear Vicky – hope you like the postcard – one of the tamer ones from Dad's collection. I should be delighted to have dinner with you: thank you for the invitation. Shall I bring some apples from the orchard? We've a glut of egremont russets. Best wishes – Mark

꿍

Cherry Tree Cottage, 18th November

Dear Hugo,

Thank you for your email. I have nothing to say about Victoria Beazley. You seem to consider her resignation a disaster. I, on the other hand, see it as an opportunity to close ranks and redouble our efforts.

I did indeed contact the Telegraph. I make no apologies when M.S. is walling up views and stretching out barbed wire. Is he preparing for a siege?

It is still possible to save Little Spinney. I cannot pretend to be disinterested. Gerald meant to share his garden with the world, yet his son, who boasts of his progressive views, wishes to turn it into a private wilderness. Little

Spinney is not the repository of his memories only. In the years of my parents' final illnesses, walking its paths and charting its development was my only solace.

I remain your friend and fellow trustee,

Marjorie

෨

Little Spinney, 21ˢᵗ November

Dear Connie,

As you can see, I am back in Berkshire. Peebles was lovely – great to see some of the old gang – but I feel my life is here now. We've had our first frost and I'm making use of a mild weekend to plant out daffodil bulbs. It seems ironic that Dad, of all people, should have been indifferent to *Narcissi*.

Did I tell you that Vicky Beazley has resigned? It's hardly a surprise. Sitting down with another of Dad's old flames must have made her feel past it, poor thing. Marjorie T. is still on the warpath. Now she has Ken Godfrey on my case. Claims he used to play golf with Dad at Wentworth. A frightful snob and something of a lush. We should prepare ourselves for a public drubbing. We are, after all, ungrateful children. There seems little point explaining that Dad conceived his garden with more love than went into our making.

I had a phone call this evening from Colonel Pickthorn. Seems his wife is very ill – a stroke. He sounded shaken up, the poor old boy. I suggested he take a break from his duties as chair of the Trust. I hope he does.

To end on a cheerier note, I look forward to hearing about your first scan! I hope it goes well. In the meantime, picture me in the hollowed out library, sitting before the seed catalogue, about to turn my mind to the delectable task of beginning afresh.

M x

Curran's Boy

Rosalind Hudis

Mackie

When my daddy drowned, I thought death might be infectious. I thought my mammy might catch it – that she might walk out of the kitchen one day, leaving the potatoes boiling and the herring half-gutted and baby Siobhan bawling for her soother, walk out into the lake under the mountain that holds still as an owl's eye. I thought they'd bring back her body, like my Da's, but with less to know her by. I thought, if I took my sights off them, mammy and Siobhan and the twins, Rose and Teresa, they'd slip away.

People say I'm the ghost of my Dad. *Mackie, poor Jimmy Curran's boy – the living image.* There's a second's panic when they see me. I was fifteen when he went. That morning I'd been walking along the strand with Evie. I had an arm around her waist. I wanted to find somewhere hidden in the dip of the dunes where we could lie down and I could stroke under her shirt. We'd reached the stretch where a stream cuts across the beach. You could always smell peat rising off it like a tang that shouldn't be there. And sheep's piss as well. The mountain smell, leaking down onto the beach. I was trying to impress Evie, make her think we were somehow heroic, me and my daddy - going out on the flood-tide to fish for flounder between Gola Island and Inishinny, setting the lobster pots in all weathers. I was lying. He didn't take risks. Not the sort of risks that take you up to an edge. I lied about the Northern Lights as well. I told her we'd seen them flecking the sky above Inishowen.

You did?

Yeah, lots of green and purple flashes – spooked me.

Evie believes most things. She looks more Irish than most of the real ones, although it's only on Donal her dad's side, the red, curling hair. She hates it. When I first met her she tried to straighten it, or dye it black, but the red always shone through and I liked that. She was touchy about her da – defending him one minute, raging the next. The locals gossiped about him. He'd left when she was four and she told me that even that young she'd felt like she was the one taking care of things.

Her folk are blow-ins; they split almost as soon as they settled out here. He's an artist, living up under the mountain. I snuck up their once to see his paintings. He was holding an open day. There were some pretty straight-forward ones – local lakes and hills, for the tourists. That kind of thing. But then we went into a different room, very light, smooth, bleached walls like the sea had got in there. Someone said this was where his real stuff was. All the canvasses were huge.

232

There was one of him, up close, all blacks and dark reds. He looked scared - tormented. But the other paintings were different: like you were looking down on the sea from some height that kept changing, as if you were a gull or someone falling very slowly. And what you saw wasn't the way a fisherman sees or feels the sea – it was like you were just seeing the pattern of it, the ebb tide coiling out to the horizon and disappearing. It made me feel free.

I tried to talk to Evie about the pictures; I thought it was a way to get more hold on her, but she'd shrug or ruffle my hair and tell me I sounded like a poofter. For some reason I thought of them as we were standing by the stream, kicking a flattened coke can around.

I said: we should go see your daddy sometimes.

What for - so he can show off his new girlie? Get a life, Mackie.

And she pulled me over the stream and into the dunes. Later the clouds moved in - dark, banked sheets. Salty drops of rain began to spit into our eyes and mouths. I pulled my jacket over both of us and we carried on. We didn't hear the men calling for me, down the beach.

Every other memory of that time flips about like dying fish - as if the days themselves were struggling to breath. I don't know what came first. There's rain, shouting, the Garda crowding into our kitchen; there's the newspaper report that keeps flashing up in front of all the other memories like a bad weather warning. No one really knows what happened or why his boat went over. He was out crabbing for the fishery. He didn't take risks. I thought over and over about what he would have seen and heard and felt in the boat as it headed out - smells of fish-guts and petrol and sea and salt and his own sweat under it all, the waves up-close, slopping against the boat, spattering against his cheeks and his hands red raw and freezing, guiding the motor, thinking moment to moment. I couldn't get further than that; I'd start to feel giddy and a bit sick and then a black panic hit me so I stopped thinking of the death at all, just that I needed to watch everyone. I needed to be careful for my whole family. I thought, I have to keep everything the same, so death can't leak in, like the bog smell from the mountain, and smuggle us away. No risks. No going on the sea.

*

Evie said: my dad's getting married – would you believe that? That hippy chick from the States. She's six years older than me. I don't want to go up there Mackie.

It's his birthday, Evie – you should go.

Jesus, Mackie, when did you get to be so holy?

But then she wrapped an arm around his neck and pushed her face into it.

Mackie, she said, come down Roarke's with me tonight. Have a drink! Your mammy's getter stronger.

Mackie kissed her hard to drown the ghost of salt and fish and petrol that blew out of nowhere and slapped across his heart.

Evie

Evie's pissed. She knows she is. She must be. Some joker, one of the Sweeney boys maybe, must have spiked her juice. Somehow she's come outside the bar. There's a taste of chips in her mouth; her lips sting – so at some point, earlier, they must have eaten, her and the crowd from Dunlewy. Party night, someone celebrating - what? What the hell's to celebrate? Too much vinegar. It's rained again. The pavements shine, lights jigging in the puddles. A man lurches out of the doorway behind her, veers towards her, splurts out something offensive then vomits near her feet, before folding up against the wall. The sharp stench clears her head for a minute. She needs to get away, down to the shore.

The midsummer sunset has spilt itself over the sea like treacle, leaking from shore to horizon. It looks strange: close to, there are dark patches on the water – stormy looking. But further out it's a luminous, cradle blue. That's how she thinks of it. Evie can see the Islands – they look painted on, almost transparent. But she doesn't want to think about paintings. Her dad's had an exhibition in the posh new gallery. Evie's looked at the flier – it showed one of the paintings; very faint, milky patterns in the sea as the tide folded back, but seen from this great distance so that everything seemed slowed and unreal. It made her feel weird, as if he'd moved ways away from all of them, gone beyond an edge. Gone beyond her. She remembered playing on he beach with him and all the kids from John and Siobhan's – years ago. Before he left. He'd built a boat of sand, big enough for them all to clamber in; they were shouting, jumping in and out, him acting the maggot, pirates, waving invisible machetes. And then, as suddenly, he was gone, bored, beyond them, ways away up the beach. She can still feel the thrill drain out of her.

That other time – out with him in the strip of goat-chewed grass and reeds that did for their garden. She must have been very small because she was racing between his legs, first one way, then the other, screaming with laughter. And then the shock, her world withering to a gasp as water poured over her face, into her eyes and mouth and ears. He'd thrown the rain bucket over her. In the stillness before she cried - that seemed to last forever but was maybe only a few seconds – she smelt bitter peat and sheep's piss all around her. She'd retched.

There's a small boat up on the sand, the oars pulled in. Mick Sweeney's. She still feels dizzy, but not so much that two plans can't get in there, into the space between daytime sense and a wilful spark - *a bit of dad* is how she thinks of it – the prankster, the risk taker. She's almost certain now it was Mike put something in the drink. She'll take his boat out – it's calm, there'll be enough light for a few more hours. Mackie's told her it's an easy row to Inishbofin Island, twenty minutes at the most, easy to pull up on its shingle beaches. They were going to do it before the accident. Before Mackie changed.

It takes her longer. Her hands are beginning to blister as the island looms up ahead. She sees tooth shaped rocks jutting out from the west side; there's spume flying off them, flame edged in the dwindling light. She thinks the currents must be powerful on that side- it wouldn't take much wind to nudge the boat towards them. When she climbs out onto the beach she's sobered enough to know she can't make it back before dark. And the wind's getting up; there are white-caps now. Riding further out across water that already looks blacker. The beach rises to a scrub of sand and maram grass and sea thrift riddled by holes – rabbit tunnels, their dried, sweet smelling pellets everywhere under-foot. Evie sees a ruin, not much more than a doorway and two windows, with the remains of a corrugated roof. We could have done it there, she thinks, me and Mackie, lying down there on our coats, risking it. We' could have made a fire and sat there looking back at the mainland. It was hard to reach him, ever since his daddy went. It felt like she was always slagging him to get out of himself.

There's still a taste of alcohol at the back of her throat, the edges of the rocks and shingle are dancing, nothing quite settling.

Mike Sweeney.

She pushes his boat back out into the sea, watches as it's tugged away, dipping, distorted towards the rocks, then she walks unevenly towards the ruin. There's her other plan. She wants Mackie to find her. It's as simple as that.

Three Poems
Frederick Pollack

PROMENADE

My friends are not in time.
They appear as statues
in an unfashionable neoclassical mode.
Postures, expressions of courage, intelligence,
fear, comradeship, laughter,
and, more embarrassing,
the vacuity of moments between these.
(The metal smile and wave of some Dear Leader
would be easier to view as art.)
The gleaming whiteness and blank eyes
come from their oblique position
vis-à-vis time, the *field* they are trapped in
or we are. Veins, like veins
in marble, are latent
compromise and doubt
they need never feel or reject.
Michelangelo said the form was imprisoned

in the stone; his role was to set it free.

Perhaps he heard a faint sound,

near-words, a low rumble

because they are too slow, or a subtle keening

because they're faster than time.

I bend to them, I try to make it out,

which must look pretty silly.

Sillier if others could see them.

MEMORIES OF MUNICH

"I think," he said self-servingly,

"genius arrives when you realize

what you can't do. Then you must choose

to shatter and deform yourself against it

or to pretend

your insights are those of the cosmos at large,

are wider than those of the cosmos.

Rilke spoke of laying the features of man

on the scale of the stars, but who's to say

the stars would accept them?

Really, you know which way the scales would tilt."

He was saying this sotto voce

to one of Otto Mueller's slinky

nudes with Kalmuk eyes and killer cheekbones,

straddling a stream

or splayed along a branch in a pastel jungle.

As if, he thought, a new Asian drift

had entered emptied lands in a warmer world.

(Then he read that Mueller's mother

may have been Roma – "*tzigeunerin*"

said the wall-card.)

Love, instantaneous. But also relief

that she was safe in a painting;

her flat gaze said

he had never been so at ease with his clothes off.

Leaving the Lenbachhaus, he walked

among hipsters, hard-chargers, cheeseburgers.

It was America. He didn't mind.

Had traveled a lot, but mostly for art.

The past, where he also traveled,

was different here, but what of that?

An American question. There is no other world;

what you see

is cool if it convincingly fakes one.

Pedestrians bumped him, gazing at their phones.

THAT WENT WELL

What happened? No windows
fall or flames erupt
from upper floors, no helicopters circle.
Suits and pantsuits
smoke-free, untorn, executives
emerge, unhysterical,
from the lobby. Some immediately phone;
some have been on their tablets since
the stairs. They breathe
heavily, but not from anthrax.
Except for underlings, temps, the clueless,
they don't talk to each other, look
around or even relieved;
were too frighteningly near stasis, which
is poverty. The street becomes the office.

Scientists, professors, bureaucrats
from lower levels, torn from less
important terminals, permit themselves
speculation: was it
an incident? The private life?
Internalised, internal terrorism?

A memo? They observe how passersby

jostle *them* more

than anybody from an upper floor.

Some adjunct/lab assistant/techie with

a vague grin and insuperable

debt gets swept off

in the flow. His superiors

ponder bi-monthly reviews and what

just now their faces are supposed to show.

Now, slightly imaging a ship's

captain evacuating last, but mostly

enraged, the owner comes. His car waits.

He has had about enough.

Tomorrow he'll be in New Zealand, in

a former wheatfield cum failed

Mitsubishi golfcourse cum House,

with a view of the Southern Alps,

and wine, guards, guns, fences and generators.

Natural selection

will replace these fools with something proudly

servile, make his wealth a stable

power, air as free as in his Bentley

from the fetor of a literate middle class.

Whose Story is This Anyway?
Jo Mazelis

That next day, a Saturday, a black-bordered envelope came in the post. Moth's great aunt Audrey had died. The funeral was in Brighton the following Wednesday. Moth, whose real name was Mary Olivia Theresa Hazeldine, had spent many unhappy summers living with her aunt after her father had disappeared in 1947.

She spent the afternoon shopping on Ealing Broadway for funeral wear. It was harder than one might have thought finding black clothes as that year navy was all the rage, but eventually she settled on a simple sheath dress in black with white polka dots, black court shoes and a single strand necklace of seed pearls. When she looked in the changing room mirror she saw someone who might have starred in a Hitchcock film (though she had never seen a Hitchcock film, only the photographs of scenes in the display case outside the cinema). To hide her dry (if not cold and triumphant) eyes she bought a pair of sunglasses with large squarish lenses and tortoiseshell rims and a black silk headscarf. Jackie O, she thought. Or maybe that infamous girl, Christine Keeler -

ducking into court, the elements of disguise hiding not grief, but guilt.

At Victoria, a guard, mistakenly and with the great courtesy of not inspecting her ticket, opened the door to the first class carriage and she, not wishing to embarrass him, sat down and arranged herself elegantly in the window seat. The carriage was almost empty, dotted here and there were men in suits who tinkered with paperwork and whose cuffs were uniformly clean and crisp. She checked her watch and then retrieved a slip of paper from her handbag to review her booking at the Grand Hotel as well as the time and address of the funeral.

The train began to move slowly, when it had picked up a little speed, the door to her carriage opened and on a faint air of London must, a man blew in and sat in a flurry of mackintosh and briefcase and newspaper in the seat opposite hers. He seemed not to have noticed that she was already occupying that table, or that the one across the aisle was empty. She saw him do a double take when he noticed her; his eyes, large with surprise, went from her to the other free seats, to the heap of possessions he'd thrown beside him. Then he shook his head, smiled to himself and looked directly at her.

'Do you mind?'

Moth took off her dark glasses. 'No, of course not.' She placed the glasses in their case, arranged the slip of paper so that it was perfectly aligned with the case.

'That's where I'm staying – The Grand,' he said. Then, seeing her alarmed expression he added, 'Sorry. That was rather impertinent, wasn't it?'

'Well ...' she said, uncertain whether to tick him off or accept the apology.

'Business trip?' he said, his eyes seeming to swarm from her face to her bosom to the slip of paper in front of her.

Before he could read the details of the funeral, she folded the note and put it back in a zippered compartment in her bag.

'Yes.'

'We could share a taxi to the hotel,' he said - very distinctly.

But somehow she heard, *We could share a room at the hotel.*

'I beg your pardon?'

'I'll pay, of course,' he added in all innocence.

'Good God,' she thought. 'He's mistaken me for a prostitute!' But, trying to make a joke of it, said, 'Are you sure you can afford it?'

He laughed and patted the back of her hand. A deal had been struck it seemed.

Great Aunt Audrey used to say that Moth was sly, that she should be watched as she had 'come-to-bed' eyes.

He picked up his newspaper. Moth, replacing her dark glasses as if the sun was catching her eyes, she took a good hard look at him. She guessed him to be in his mid to late thirties, trim and healthy looking. He had a good head of dark blonde hair, no grey that she could see, a longish face and square chin, a modest nose, small mouth, with pale, flesh-coloured lips. Eyebrows and lashes that were darker than his hair.

As if he was suddenly aware of her gaze, he looked up and said brightly, 'Have you been to The Royal Pavilion?'

'Oh well, not since I was a child…'

'Never been! Not in all the years I've been coming down – can you believe that?'

'Well…'

'It's not the sort of thing you do on your own is it? I mean there should be someone with you, or else you'd look like an odd fish.'

His eyes were brown with flecks of gold, his teeth small, white and even.

'What do you think? Want to save a chap from looking like an odd fish?'

'I'm not sure.'

'Oh, say you will. We'll hop in a cab, drop our bags at the hotel, go straight to the Pavilion. Tell the boss the train was delayed, eh?'

The ticket inspector arrived. Her travelling companion reached into his inside pocket and presented his ticket, then both men turned to her. She took out her purse and without hesitation handed over her second-class ticket.

'You're in the wrong carriage. Plenty of seats in second,' the inspector said and indicated with a hand as stiff as a wooden signal the way out of the first class compartment.

'Oh, for goodness sake, man! We'll be there in less than twenty minutes! You're surely not going to insist the lady move seats now?'

The guard muttered something that she did not hear as it seemed a shrill buzzing had filled her ears and her heart flapped like a fish on mud flats deep in the dark estuary of her chest.

'Let me pay the difference. I'm sure this is just some mistake on the part of the booking office. How much do you want for the lady?'

How much do you want for the lady? That was an odd way of putting it. Money passed between the two men, disappearing into the guard's pocket with seamless speed. No new ticket was issued.

Now she really had been bought, there was no getting away from it.

There was the funeral to consider. Two o'clock on Bear Road. The train got in at twelve-forty; she had planned a taxi to the hotel to drop off her bag, then back in the same cab to the service.

She had a picture of herself at the graveside, handfuls of earth in her palm, then the soft stammering sound as they were cast on the coffin. Her come-to-bed eyes as dry as old bread crust behind the black insect eyes of her sunglasses.

Audrey had loved to talk about her own death, as if it were the fulcrum on which all good and evil depended. Moth grew very tired of the predictions flung at her by Audrey; 'You'll be sorry, you'll rue the day. When I'm gone, then you'll know!'

She had been thinking of this and gazing with a frown out of the window when she glimpsed the green swathes of The Downs rolling lyrically by.

'So... the Pavilion?' the man said, smiling hopefully.

'I can't I'm afraid.'

'No?'

'I have an appointment I can't miss.'

'Later this afternoon, then? Tomorrow?'

'Hm... maybe.'

'I see,' he said and seemed to withdraw into himself. He fussed with his newspaper, then hid behind it and pretended to be engrossed in it for the rest of the journey.

As they neared the station, he stood up and gathered his belongings and without another word made his way to the exit.

Outside the station she saw several taxis pull away and by the time she reached the rank none were waiting.

Convinced that she had done nothing to make him become so cold towards her she turned the whole episode over and over in her mind until she had rehashed it entirely from a romance into a melodrama so ensnaring and deceptive and deadly that she felt sure she was lucky to escape with her life. He was a killer, a sadistic rapist preying on the sort of woman who could afford a first class ticket. He was in cahoots with the inspector. And as for that charade of him being the last to board the train and thus being so flustered he sat with her instead of at any of the other empty seats! Why, he'd probably been on the train long before her, sizing her up. All he had to do was open and close the door, then scurry distractedly up the aisle and throw himself down opposite.

But, given such an elaborate plot, why had he given it up so abruptly? She looked around her, half expecting to see him waiting for her, watching.

A cab drew up and the driver got out, popped the boot, came around the car and stooped to pick up her bag. Panicking she snatched it out of his reach.

'I've changed my mind,' she said imperiously. 'I'll walk.'

'Suit yer bleeding self, Mrs!' he called after her and she felt his anger like so many poisoned darts in her back. It was not a very long walk to the Grand on the seafront and her bags were not heavy; the key reason for getting a cab was timing. It was the matter of not only getting to the hotel but getting to the funeral on time.

Having marched at a furious pace down West Street, she now slowed, calculating not only the business of checking in, then finding another taxi, but also the fact of her whereabouts being known. He, or rather *they* - for he had his henchmen, would be waiting for her at the hotel, and despite the Grand's gracious reputation, it was very possible that a bell boy or kitchen porter was also in on the scheme.

Was this not what Audrey had always warned her about? 'When I'm gone, then you'll know!' and with this thought an even more elaborate plot was revealed to her in all its nail-biting horror, its vengeful calculation. All of this was Audrey's concoction; she had planned it from beyond the grave, hiring these men with her long hoarded pounds, shillings and pence, in order to be proved unequivocally right with her bitter old predictions. To be certain to have the last word.

Or Audrey was not dead at all. Not yet. She was hovering on the brink, as enlivened by this last act of cruelty as Lazarus by the presence of Christ. This was her sanatorium of good air, this her penicillin, her youth-giving sacred fire.

No. Moth checked herself. It was too much. A flight of fancy as preposterous as those she'd had as a girl.

Such as when she had seen the strange man staring in at her from the window in Audrey's house and later smelled the smoke from his cigar drifting from Audrey's bedroom. The guest room and Audrey's bedroom were linked by a long balcony that overlooked the drive, the defunct fountain and the incorruptible lawns, and a man might easily have walked along it to spy on her.

'This child's imagination must be checked,' Audrey had instructed her mother sternly the next day. She had then gone on to offer such a terrible and detailed account of her mother's shortcomings as a parent that both Moth and her mother and the lady's companion whom Audrey had hired that year, a beautiful young TB sufferer called Helen, were all moved to crescendos of weeping.

Moth had been drawn to Helen – even her name carried the freight of tragedy – she was Helen Keller the blind, deaf and dumb girl, and Helen of Troy and Helen Burns, Jane Eyre's dearest friend who had died in her arms. Only once had Moth had the opportunity to be alone with Helen and that had been short-lived. She had wandered into the walled kitchen garden behind the house and found Helen collecting herbs for a tisane. Shyly, Moth had crept closer and closer and was rewarded with a friendly smile.

'Smell this,' said Helen and she rubbed a leaf between her fingers then offered it to Moth.

'Lemons!'

'That's lemon verbena. Here, what's this?'

'Lavender!'

'Good and this one?'

She let Moth cut some of the stems and showed her how she laid them neatly in rows at the bottom of the wooden trug. She explained their use in medicine and their symbolism; twelve sage leaves picked at midnight for divination, bay leaves to ward off evil, coriander as a love potion.

If a child is capable of falling deeply and everlastingly in love, then Moth fell into that beautiful condition at that moment. Add the drone of bees, the great aching canopy of intensely blue sky above, the pungent perfume of the flowers, the sun warming her pale and winter-starved skin, and Helen's kind but tragic beauty, and all becomes clear.

The sound of a cane rapped on a metal gate caused both of them to jump. Moth turned to see Audrey, her mouth set in a hard fleshless line, her eyes small and black and bright, her chin raised. Helen quickly rose to her feet and gathered up the scissors and the trug with hands that were visibly trembling. Audrey slowly raised the cane as if it were a divining rod set to sniff out evil then started toward them. Helen hurried off, ducking as she passed Audrey as though she expected the cane to fall upon her shoulders. Moth stood where she was, rigid with fear. She was seven years old.

She never dared to approach Helen again, but looked at her often with baleful helpless eyes. Helen avoided the child's gaze, her touch, the very breath from her lips – for she *had been warned*. Then not long after Helen was gone and was never spoken of by anyone in the house again.

'Then you'll know!'

Moth seemed to hear the old woman's voice and sensed the whip-like shadow of her cane flickering impatiently like a branch against the moon. 'That child lets her imagination run riot. She is in mortal danger; the devil will find use for her and make no mistake!'

The song of Audrey's words was constant, a noise that went on echoing and ringing in the ears and mind long after the tongue had ceased its flapping.

What had she, Moth ever done to attract such suspicion? She had been far too young for the depravity and cunning of which she was accused, far too young to cast off the wolf's skin thrown upon her and see it as a thing apart. She was a lamb unbloodied in the ripe pasture of the world, and yet the weight of the predator's disguise crippled and disfigured her. She had no chance to grow up straight and tall and true no matter how she strived after goodness.

There was no changing anything, the damage was done. A taxi was on its way up the road to the station, she waved to it and the driver made a u-turn causing another driver to blast his horn. This seemed to prove to her that an alteration in plans always created discord somewhere.

'To the Grand,' she said. 'Then on to Bear Road.'

He was not one of those chatty taxi drivers who felt compelled to discuss the weather or the state of the world. He had a set of beads hanging from his driver's mirror that she at first took for a rosary, then thought better of it, as his look, sallow skin and a great head of grey black curls told her otherwise. There was a photo fixed to his dashboard; dark-haired girls in brightly coloured party frocks, gathered around an older woman. She would have liked to have a conversation about these girls, ask how old they were now and did he also have sons and if not, was that a sorrow to him? But she had a way of turning such friendly queries into an interrogation, of setting a person on edge.

She ran into the hotel and gave her bag to reception as her room was not yet ready. She half expected to bump into the man from the train, but then he must be off, padding respectfully around the Royal Pavilion, standing behind a fat silky scarlet rope, peering at an elaborately curtained bed or columns topped with copper palm leaves. She should have gone with him, saved him from being – what had he said – an odd fish.

Back in the cab, she fastened her seat belt and as the driver pulled off she said, 'Those are your daughters, I suppose.'

'They are no daughters of mine,' he said and shook his head, denying and disowning them with such vehemence, that she felt afraid.

She was entirely ignorant of the fact that certain taxi drivers shared their vehicles with others; that this man sat with these prayer beads and the photograph of the woman and her five nameless daughters day after day with no more relationship to them than to the steering wheel or the gear stick. Nor could she know that his English, still a strange meat on his tongue had been half-learned from Shakespeare and Dickens as he sat beneath drying octopus in his father's taverna in Chania, Crete.

Her vision grew blurred as tears poured from her eyes and the unfamiliar streets seemed to flash past in a riddle. She had no idea where she was, where he was taking her.

At last he slowed the engine. 'Bear Road,' he said. 'What number?'

A long row of houses stood on one side of the road with a featureless tall grey stone wall opposite. Above the wall the tops of trees could be seen, green and dense and giving no indication of what lay beyond.

'I don't know,' she said and thought, do cemeteries have numbers? Or churches? Or crematoriums? She opened her handbag to find the paper with all the details, but it was gone. He brought the car to a standstill and turning in his seat said, 'It's a long road.' A car honked its horn behind them and he drove a little further until he found a place to pull in. A long black hearse sailed majestically past, the coffin in the back engulfed by flowers. Four more gleaming limousines followed.

'It's a funeral,' she said. 'Follow them.'

He raised his hands in despair, but tagged onto the tail of the procession. Further up the road the cars turned one after another and poured through a wide gate in the wall.

The taxi followed pulling up behind a long line of cars. She paid the driver and instantly forgetting her distrust of him, tipped him generously. Gathering herself, smoothing her dress, she walked unsteadily towards the small black-clad gathering. People nodded at her or smiled the strange sad smiles of greeting reserved for funerals. Many of the mourners were youngish, smart and good looking; there was no one over fifty or sixty that she could see. Many of the people dabbed at their eyes or consoled one another with tender gestures; pats on the back, a hug, a long held handshake. More cars arrived, Bentleys and Wolseleys and Jaguars, disgorging another thirty or so people.

Moth felt a pinch of jealousy, if she died how many would attend her funeral? And what would they look like? A hodge podge, a rabble in fraying suits worn for weddings, christenings, job interviews and funerals for year after year, or not wearing black at all, but maroon, like her mother, who had only one good winter coat.

She turned to watch the men slide the coffin from the hearse and began to hear the name Freddie peppering the air around her in many conversations. Freddie or Frederick or darling Fred. Or poor Fred. Brave Fred. And it dawned on her: she was at the wrong funeral.

As the mourners made their way inside, Moth walked back to Bear Road. Once there she stopped and looked around, aghast. There were *three* cemeteries very close to one another, all with different names. How could this be? She had the sensation that someone was watching her confusion and discomfort, laughing behind their hand.

'*Then* you'll know.'

The words were always there. Then you'll *know*. Then *you'll* know.

'Know what?' she said angrily, her voice strange to her at this crossroad of death, so manicured and suburban under a blue afternoon sky. 'You never said, Audrey. What will I know?'

At the entrance gates she passed from the dazzling light into the shadow of the trees and found that she could barely see. She hesitated a moment uncertain of her direction, aching for all the lost opportunities of her life, and particularly the most recent. She saw herself in the cool rooms of the Royal Pavilion, a gentleman by her side, cupping her elbow as he pointed to some detail in the hand-painted wallpaper. Then stumbling blindly, desperate now to be gone she stepped into the road and straight into t

he path of the hearse bearing her aunt's coffin. The driver was late and as there were no cars following him he was driving at a less than stately pace.

Moth remembered now the beautiful chinoiserie wallpaper that must have lodged in some bright corner of her mind since childhood; a bird, the Paradise Flycatcher perhaps, rising up in the air in an explosion of energy and colour, its long tail feathers like gay, powder-blue ribbons. And she, Moth flew up in air and only when she fell to earth did she finally know everything.

Spaces Only I Know
Clodagh O'Brien

I know the spaces too small for him. The gaps and holes only I can fit into. I'm in one now, the cubbyhole under the stairs, misted with cobwebs too torn to be homes. Above me floorboards creak. Swarms of dust wheeze out, hang in the dark as galaxies. I close my eyes and see stars. They dance on my eyelids and bring me away.

I'm in a forest, feet on cold moss. The moon slides through the trees and turns trunks silver. There's a huge cat, its body bent over a puddle lapping up mouthfuls. I walk closer, careful of twigs and branches. Across the cat's back are gashes, skin slashed to reveal sausages of muscle. Moonbeams glint across them as knives. I reach out, my hand over its back. Heat rises in a wave. Red coats my fingers. The cat jumps and hisses, a violent gush sound.

"I'm sorry. Sorry." I draw back my hand.

It takes my apologies curiously; drops wet lips over black teeth. "Why do you touch me?"

"To see if you're okay," I answer.

"Isn't it obvious I'm not?"

I pause, my mind frozen by such a truth.

The cat tilts its head: "How did you get here?"

I try to remember where I came from. "I don't know. I just did."

The cat sits, tail whipping the ground in snaky strokes. It turns to its back, licks the cuts in a way that must hurt.

"You're not from here are you?" I ask.

The licks pause. "Not at first."

"And now?"

"Now I wouldn't know where else to be."

Thumps shake the stairs. My eyes spring open. The scooter by the wall rattles, the wheels patchy with rust. I used to ride it, in circles outside the house. I'd sneak down to the gate and peer out. Out there the trees were taller, the flowers plumper, the sun brighter.

"Melanie?"

That's not my name, but it's what he calls me.

"Get out here." He's using his no-nonsense voice, the one that used to scare me.

Boots clunk across the floor. I can smell him; damp as if left out in the rain too long. Everything goes cold. His breath creeps through the door. I squeeze my eyelashes to block him out.

I'm back in the forest, back with the cat: "How long have you been here?"

The cat lies down, paws stretched out. "Longer than I remember."

"Did you want to come here?"

"It wasn't my place to say no," replies the cat.

I sit down, the moss soft beneath. We're eye to eye, yellow to blue.

"And you?" the cat enquires. "When did you start coming here?"

"After I found my things," I admit, "in one of my spaces. A coat, hat and bag with my name on it."

The cat nods, rests its chin on a paw. From its back a chunk of bone pokes out. "I was a cub when I came here, with my two brothers. But, they are somewhere else now. I stay here in case they come back."

I smile to fill the quiet. We both know too much to keep believing.

His fist pounds the cubbyhole: "I'll smash this open if you don't come out."

I know he won't. The house is what keeps him safe.

"Melanie." He spreads my name like marmalade.

I try not to move. His footsteps fade. Soon he'll be in the kitchen, the gas flickering under a frying pan. The fridge will be opened and bacon laid out in strips, their edges crisping. An egg will nudge beside them, its yellow centre turning hard as a button. Spits and crackles will make my stomach rumble. I press my forehead to my knees and rock.

There's no moon when I arrive. "Are you still here?"

The cat mumbles, its voice a tremble: "Is that you brother?"

I see a back of bones, fur and skin dripping away. "It's just me," I whisper.

The cat looks up, eyes dull as sand. I sit down beside it, my hand across its head.

"What's your name?" the cat asks.

"What?"

"Your name. You said you saw it on the things you found. In one of your spaces."

I've never said it aloud before. My heart stops to hear. "Cara. My name is Cara."

"Pretty. That's a pretty name."

I feel a tear and let it come. It drops onto whiskers.

"Well Cara, I think it's time for you to go home."

"Home?"

"Yes, home."

"But what if I can't find it?"

The cat moves beneath me. Struggles to its feet, back clacking. "Believe me, you won't find it here."

I watch the cat go, tail tall and proud.

"But I'm scared," I murmur.

Back in the house the frying pan thumps. The gas clicks. He hums; a song I recognise, but don't know. I crawl out of the cubbyhole. Sun coats the floorboards and I tiptoe across its stripes. The bacon spits out its saltiness. I pull the front door open, my skin warmed by a cloud-free sky. I take a breath that feels like my first.

"Greedy, greedy always gets you out." He's behind me, a fork in hand.

I run, my soles pinched by stones and stubbed by rocks. He screams after me, his boots slowed by surprise. I reach the gate. The trees are fat with leaves, bees busy over flowers, sun pouring down.

"Get back here!" he yells.

I turn; look at the face that's claimed me all these years. It's old, shrivelled by his wrongs. I pick up a rock and throw. For all the times spent beneath him. For the spaces I had to find. It clunks his forehead. Blood trickles into his eyes. I spit him out, a streak of froth between us.

"I'm going home," I roar.

I clamber over the gate. I run.

Contributors

Carole Burns' book of short stories, *The Missing Woman*, is being published in April by Parthian Books. She is a reviewer for the Washington Post and editor of *Off the Page: Writers Talk About Beginnings, Endings, and Everything in Between*, a book based on interviews with 43 writers including Andrea Levy, Colm Tóibín, Richard Ford, and A.S. Byatt. She is Head of Creative Writing at the University of Southampton.

Liam Cagney an Irish author, music critic and musicologist. His fiction has been published in *The Moth*, *The Honest Ulsterman*, and elsewhere, and he has a hybrid fiction/essay coming up in the next issue of *Gorse*. His criticism has been published in *The Daily Telegraph*, *Opera Magazine*, and elsewhere. He is an ex-editor of the online journal *Colony*

Chris Cornwell studied Philosophy at the University of Wales, Trinity Saint David. His poems have been published by *Wales Arts Review* and *The Lampeter Review* amongst others.

Dan Coxon is the editor of Litro magazine and the author of *Ka Mate: Travels in New Zealand*, which was used as background research for the ITV documentary *River Deep, Mountain High*. My writing has previously appeared in Salon, The Portland Review, Neon, Gutter, 3:AM, The Nervous Breakdown, The Weeklings, and in the DadLit anthology *Daddy Cool*, amongst others.

Armel Dagorn is now back in his native France after living in Ireland for seven years. His writing has appeared in magazines such as *The Stinging Fly*, *Tin House online*, *Southword*, *The Penny Dreadful* and *Popshot*.

Stevie Davies, who comes from Morriston, Swansea, is a novelist, literary critic, biographer and historian. She is a Fellow of the Royal Society of Literature, a Fellow of the Academi Gymreig and Professor of Creative Writing at the University of Wales, Swansea. A collection of Stevie's short fiction, *'Arrest Me, for I have run away'*, will be published by Parthian in 2016. Her latest novel is *Awakening*.

Rachel J Fenton was born in South Yorkshire and moved to Auckland's North Shore in 2007 to write *Some Things the English,* which was a finalist in the 2014 Dundee International Book Prize. She is the winner of Short Fiction's seventh annual competition (in association with the University of Plymouth).

Jamie Guiney is a literary fiction writer from County Armagh, Northern Ireland. His short stories have been published internationally and he has been nominated twice for the 'The Pushcart Prize' with his stories 'A Quarter Yellow Sun' and 'The Cowboy.' Jamie is a graduate of the Faber & Faber Writing Academy and has twice been a judge for short story competition 'The New Rose Prize.' His work has been backed by the Northern Ireland Arts Council through several Individual Artist Awards. He tweets as @jamesgwriter

Patrick Holloway is currently completing his PhD in Brazil in Creative Writing, where he is writing a bilingual book of poetry. His story 'A Long Haul' was chosen for the anthology 'Kissing Him Goodbye and other stories', by Poetic Republic. His poem 'A Ritual' was recently published in the anthology 'We Will Be Shelter.' His other stories and poems have been published by a host of literary journals including Overland Literary Journal and Poetry Ireland Review. His short story Counting Stairs was highly commended for the Manchester Fiction Prize.

Nigel Jarrett is a winner of the Rhys Davies Prize for short fiction. His first story collection, Funderland, was published to wide acclaim, notably in the Guardian, the Independent, and the Times. His début poetry collection, Miners At The Quarry Pool, was published by Parthian in November 2013 and described by the New Welsh Review as 'evocative, provocative and gritty'. A former daily-newspaper journalist, he is now a freelance writer, and reviews poetry for Acumen magazine and jazz for Jazz Journal. He lives in Monmouthshire.

Jo Mazelis is the author of short stories, non-fiction and poetry. Her collection of stories, *Diving Girls* (Parthian, 2002), was short-listed for the Commonwealth 'Best First Book' and Wales Book of the Year. Her second book, *Circle Games* (Parthian, 2005), was long-listed for Wales Book of the Year. Her stories and poetry have been broadcast on BBC Radio 4 and published in various anthologies and magazines, and translated into Danish. Her latest book is *Significance* (Seren, 2014).

267

Born and educated in Swansea, Jo returned to her hometown in 1991 after working in London for many years. During the 1980s she worked as a graphic designer, photographer and illustrator for the magazines *City Limits, Women's Review, Spare Rib, Undercurrents, Everywoman* and *New Dance*.

Medbh McGuckian was born in Belfast where she lives with her family. Her collections of poetry include: *The Flower Master* (1982), *Venus and the Rain* (1984), *On Ballycastle Beach* (1988), *Marconi's Cottage* (1992), *Captain Lavender* (1995), *Shelmalier* (1998), and *Drawing Ballerinas* (2001). Her *Selected Poems 1978-1994* was published in 1997. Among the prizes she has won are: the British National Poetry Competition, the Cheltenham Award, the Alice Hunt Bartlett prize, the Rooney Prize and the American Ireland Fund Literary Award. She has been Writer-in-Residence at Queen's University and at the University of Ulster; Visiting Fellow at the University of California, Berkeley; and Writer-Fellow at Trinity College Dublin.

Anna Metcalfe was born in Holzwickede in 1987. Her stories have been published in Tender Journal, Elbow Room, Lighthouse, The Warwick Review and The Best British Short Stories 2014. In 2014, she was also shortlisted for The Sunday Times Short Story Award. She lives in Norwich, where she is working on her first collection.

Kathy Miles' work has appeared in many magazines and anthologies, and her third poetry collection, *Gardening With Deer*, will be published by Cinnamon Press in June 2016. She won the 2013 Second Light Poetry Competition and the 2014 Welsh Poetry Competition. She is currently doing an MA in Creative Writing at the University of Wales, Trinity Saint David, and is a member of the Red Heron performance group.

Alison Moore's first novel, *The Lighthouse*, was shortlisted for the Man Booker Prize 2012 and the National Book Awards 2012 (New Writer of the Year), winning the McKitterick Prize 2013. Her shorter fiction has been published in Best British Short Stories anthologies and in her debut collection *The Pre-War House and Other Stories*, whose title story won a novella prize. Her latest novel, *He Wants*, was an *Observer* Book of the Year. Born in Manchester in 1971, she lives near Nottingham with her husband Dan and son Arthur.

Gregory Norminton has published four novels, a collection of short stories and a book of aphorism. He teaches creative writing at

Manchester Metropolitan University, and lives with his wife and daughter in Sheffield. 'In My Father's Garden' will appear in his new collection of stories, THE GHOST WHO BLED, published by Comma Press in May.

Clodagh O'Brien writes flash fiction, short stories and the occasional poem. Based in Dublin, she has been published in many interesting places such as Flash: The International Short-Short Story Magazine, Litro Magazine, Literary Orphans, Flash Flood amongst others. Her flash fiction was recently highly commended at the Dromineer Literary Festival and shortlisted for the Allingham Arts Festival. She likes to write in bed, and realises there are too many books to read before she dies.

Frederick Pollack is the author of two book-length narrative poems, THE ADVENTURE and HAPPINESS, both published by Story Line Press and also a collection of shorter poems, A POVERTY OF WORDS, February 2015 from Prolific Press. He has appeared in *Hudson Review, Salmagundi, Poetry Salzburg Review, Die Gazette* (Munich), *The Fish Anthology* (Ireland), *Representations, Magma* (UK), *Iota* (UK), *Bateau, Main Street Rag, Fulcrum*, etc. Online, poems have appeared in *Big Bridge, Hamilton Stone Review, Diagram, BlazeVox, The New Hampshire Review, Mudlark, Occupoetry, Faircloth Review, Triggerfish*, etc. Adjunct professor creative writing George Washington University.

Bethany W Pope is an LBA winning author, and a finalist for the Faulkner-Wisdom Awards, the Cinnamon Press Novel competition, and the Ink, Sweat and Tears poetry commission, placed third in the Bare Fiction Poetry Competition and she was recently highly commended in this year's Poetry London Competition. She was recently nominated for the 2014 Pushcart Prize. She received her PhD from Aberystwyth University's Creative Writing program, and her MA from the University of Wales Trinity St David. She has published several collections of poetry: *A Radiance* (Cultured Llama, 2012) *Crown of Thorns,* (Oneiros Books, 2013), and *The Gospel of Flies* (Writing Knights Press 2014), and *Undisturbed Circles* (Lapwing, 2014). Her first novel, *Masque,* shall be published by Seren in 2016.

Steph Power is a London-born writer and composer who has been based in Wales for nearly three decades. As well as writing for *Wales Arts Review*, she is an opera and classical music critic for *The Independent* and a regular contributor to the new-music journal

Tempo. Further reviews, polemical essays and poetry have been published by *Planet Magazine, New Left Project, Poetry Wales, The Lonely Crowd*, and *Ink, Sweat and Tears*. Her music has been performed by PM Music Ensemble, pianist Llŷr Williams and the Bridge Duo among others. Steph is also an examiner for Trinity College, London, having been a performer specialising in 20th-Century and contemporary music at international level.

Gary Raymond is a novelist, short story writer, critic, and lecturer in English and Creative Writing. As well as a regular voice in *Wales Arts Review*, Gary has written for *The Guardian, Rolling Stone Magazine*, is a theatre critic for *The Arts Desk*, and is a regular commentator on arts and culture for BBC Wales. In 2013, Gary published *JRR Tolkien: A Visual Biography of Fantasy's Most Revered Writer* with Ivy Press, and his novel, *For Those Who Come After*, is out in October 2015 (Parthian Books).

Valerie Sirr's collection of short stories received funding from the Arts Council of Ireland under the title-by-scheme in 2014. Her short stories, short shorts, and poems are published in Ireland, UK, US, Australia and Asia. Honours include 2007 Hennessy New Irish Writer Award, Arts Council of Ireland literature bursaries, and other national and international literature awards. She holds an M. Phil. in Creative Writing from Trinity College, Dublin.

Caitlin Thomson just moved for the 15th time. Her work has appeared in numerous places, including: The Literary Review of Canada, The Moth, Going Down Swinging, and the anthology Killer Verse. Her second chapbook Incident Reports was recently released by Hyacinth Girl Press.

Tom Vowler is the editor of the literary journal, Short Fiction, and is currently working on his second collection of stories. His first, *The Method*, won the Scott Prize in 2010 and the Edge Hill Readers' Prize in 2011. His second novel, *That Dark Remembered Day*, was published last year.